Cleaning
Historic
Buildings

Volume 1
SUBSTRATES, SOILING
AND INVESTIGATIONS

Cleaning Historic Buildings

Volume 1

SUBSTRATES, SOILING AND INVESTIGATIONS

NICOLA ASHURST

DONHEAD

First published in the United Kingdom
in 1994 by
Donhead Publishing Ltd
28 Southdean Gardens
Wimbledon
London SW19 6NU
Tel. 081-789 0138

ISBN 1 873394 01 2 (Volume 1)
ISBN 1 873394 12 8 (set)

A CIP catalogue record for this book is available from the
British Library.

Typeset by Keyboard Services, Luton
Printed in Great Britain at the Alden Press,
Osney Mead, Oxford

Contents

Volume 2
CLEANING MATERIALS AND PROCESSES

Preface

For much of the twentieth century, cleaning of the masonry materials of which traditional buildings in the United Kingdom are composed has formed an integral part of conservation and repair programmes. It is likely to remain so but there is a call for a greater understanding of the need for and the effects of what is being done. Technical information has not been readily available and currently remains incomplete and scattered. This book aims to redress both situations.

The volumes are based on materials and practices common in the UK but their value and usefulness is international. Important basic principles are presented which should be considered when it is proposed that any building or structure of historic value is to be cleaned. Assessment criteria leading to the decision to clean or not to clean are considered, along with the special and individual characteristics of each of the traditional masonry materials which are commonly involved. These include sandstones, granites, limestones, brickwork, terracotta, faience, mortars and renders. The natures of the various types of soiling are described, as are the strengths and weaknesses of currently available cleaning methods.

These volumes are intended to improve the understanding of those involved in the many aspects of masonry cleaning and thereby to improve the quality of decision-making and workmanship undertaken.

They will serve professionals, advisors, building owners and practitioners by providing a sound base of information with a strong practical emphasis. They emphasize the need to investigate each situation before designing a cleaning process suited to it. They urge the need to avoid assumptions and a dependence on cleaning systems and any recommendations or cleaning systems which claim to do away with the need to understand.

Acknowledgements

I wish to thank the many people who have enabled the writing of this book and would also like to acknowledge the spiritual support I have received throughout my life. The inspiration I have gained from my faith in God and his Son, Jesus Christ, has given me the confidence and strength to develop my career and skills.

My husband, Neil Barkworth, has tirelessly supported me throughout the full pregnancy and birth of these volumes, not a small task. My secretary and friend, Eileen Flinn, turned freeform drafts into respectable text while keeping the office running at the same time.

The older I get, the more I appreciate the role of my architect father, Sergei Malnic, who took me to site from a very early age, and my photographer mother, Jutta Malnic, who persuaded me not to leave school at 16. Both continue to practise in Sydney.

Many hours of collaboration and discussion with John Kelly greatly improved my geological, technical and analytical understanding of masonry deterioration and the effects of cleaning.

Special thanks go to several people in the contracting and materials supply fields for working with me, teaching me how the theory of a specification can be translated into good cleaning practice. They include Craig Liddle, Terry Straw, Tracey Fellowes, David Ball, Peter A. Cox,

Roger Hicks, David Priestman, David Boyer, David Frost and David Odgers.

Input from the professional side has also been very significant. In Australia, this began with Jack Heiman, George Gibbons and Alan Spry. In the UK, those who must be thanked include Julian Harrap, Geoffrey Jarvis, John Fidler and many others at English Heritage, James Simpson, Frank Dimes, Philip Venning, Rachel Bower and the staff of the Society for the Protection of Ancient Buildings.

I am particularly grateful to all my clients of recent years for the honour and experience of working on their buildings.

Special thanks go to Martin Weaver for his mammoth efforts of reviewing the first draft of the text and congratulations to Jill Pearce for her persuasive diplomacy in extracting the final manuscript and providing a quality publishing service of which she should be very proud.

I would also like to thank the following for their kind permission to use material:

English Heritage
John Kelly, BSc
Gray, Marshall & Associates
Dr Trudie McMullen (Mansfield)
Dr Brian Bluck and Ms Jane Porter
Phillips Son & Neale Properties, Edinburgh
K.R. Banyard Ltd, Architects, Gateshead
Gateshead Metropolitan Borough Council
Lithan Ltd, Belfast
University of Central England in Birmingham
Associated Architects, Birmingham
Tarmac Swindon Ltd
Francis G. Dimes, MSc, BSc, MGeol, FGS
Robin W. Sanderson, BSc, FGS
The Australian Council of National Trusts
The National Trust of Australia (Victoria)

Robert Butcher
Martin Weaver
The Friends of Bath Abbey
Chris Tucker, BSc, Dip.Bldg.Cons., ARICS
Renfrew District Council, Department of Architectural and Related Services
Geoffrey Jarvis, Architect, Glasgow
The Wellington Church, Glasgow
Wirral Borough Council, Department of Planning and Economic Development
Coin Street Community Builders Ltd
Lifschutz Davidson Ltd, Architects, Hammersmith
Nottingham Community Housing Association Ltd
Kirklees Metropolitan Council, Property Services Division
Spitalfields, Development Group
Julian Harrap, Architects, London

Chapter One

Attitudes to Cleaning

1.1 NO STANDARD ANSWER

The cleaning of masonry surfaces is not only necessary for aesthetic reasons but also required to ensure better preservation of these materials. The present volumes deal with the cleaning of the traditional masonry materials – sandstones, limestones, brick and terracotta/faience – which have been soiled in external environments. In the UK, these materials have been used widely in the construction of buildings. These books aim to explain some of the complexity of their characteristics, weathering and soiling, and to provide guidelines for the assessment of the project at hand and the design of the cleaning process applicable to it. Standard answers and specifications are not provided. Whatever their context, the complexity of the safe cleaning of these materials must be evaluated in detail.

> The greatest problem in developing practical guidelines for cleaning any historic building is the large number of variable and unpredictable factors involved. Because these variables make each cleaning project unique, it is difficult to establish specific standards at this time.[1]

In fact, it would be unwise and dangerous to establish them.

1.2 STATE OF THE UK INDUSTRY

Despite the many technical advances in the field of masonry cleaning, particularly during the 1980s, there continues to be a regrettable and unnecessary number of damaging mistakes made because the necessary level of understanding is not available, and thorough, job-specific evaluations are not being done. The beginning of the 1990s has given birth to an unprecedented level of concern in the UK for the extent of damage caused to historic facades by cleaning operations. Expertise, resources and management have come under scrutiny as it has become clear that in many instances the current state of affairs is so inadequate that it would have been better if many cleaning operations had not been undertaken at all. In the midst of this sorry state of affairs, the many cleaning projects which have been undertaken to a high standard are not receiving sufficient publicity or praise to redress fully the vociferous criticism of problematic projects.

There are many reasons for what has happened and, in some quarters, continues to happen. In most instances, insufficient time and money were allocated to cleaning. Many professionals and agents responsible for masonry cleaning do not have the specialist knowledge required to make the necessary technical decisions. Contract documentation is frequently designed to shift decision-making to the contractor on site, but in many instances a limited budget and fixed price have prevented undertaking the variations necessary to make the cleaning successful. An increased dependency on 'systems' and the trade literature that accompanies them has devalued the importance of fully understanding the materials and surfaces which are to be cleaned and the soiling which is to be removed from them.

The cleaning of masonry is, and should be expected to be, a more complex and important process than it has been on many repair and refurbishment projects. Due consideration must be given to the masonry substrate, its condition, the nature and degree of soiling(s), the effect of cleaning and the appearance it will create, the effect of the cleaning at microscopic level and in relation to the future weathering of the building, the safety of the operatives, members of the public and occupants, all necessary protection and the effect of the processes on the environment. Consideration of all these aspects cannot be undertaken without proper planning, sufficient time and cost commitment. The number of variables which apply to a cleaning system means that a different system needs to be designed for each building. There may be similarities but there will always be important differences which will relate to the new situation and be important in the undertaking of a quality clean. An inappropriate system can be ineffective, cause irreparable damage, be a waste of money, or all three.

Historic building repair and conservation is acknowledged as a specialist field. The cleaning of the surfaces of such structures is even further specialized and a realm into which only a few practitioners are sufficiently trained to enter. The experience of many masonry cleaning firms needs to be similarly deepened and improved. The complexity of a successful cleaning operation must be grasped at client, main contractor and project management levels as well.

In the UK, standards of good practice are set out in the form of recommendations in BS 6270, Part 1, 1982 (with amendments), the British Standard Code of Practice for Cleaning and Surface Repair of Buildings, Part 1, Natural Stone, Carved Stone and Clay and Calcium Silicate Brick Masonry (plus Appendix G: Terracotta and Faience). A review of BS 6270, Part 1 has begun (in 1993) to reflect developments of the past decade. Principles of good practice have also been prepared by the Cleaning Sub-Committee of the UK Stone Federation, the professional body for practitioners involved in the winning, repairing and cleaning of stone. The evidence on the buildings is that these sets of guidelines are not enough.

It must nevertheless be recognized that the stone cleaning industry has formed part of the general construction industry for a long time and that considerable depths of knowledge and expertise can be found in several areas. Incompetent practitioners can be found in all professional and contracting fields, and the cleaning industry is no exception. Experienced cleaning contracting companies can be located that have demonstrated over many years quality cleaning on a range of substrates, using a range of techniques.[2] Levels of competence vary widely, however, and it is always worth establishing the expertise of a firm under consideration by inspecting previous projects.

There was increasing concern in the early 1990s for the likelihood of damage caused by the use of chemical cleaning materials. This concern stemmed from a study commissioned in response to widespread misuse of chemical cleaning processes in Scotland.

During the 1970s and 1980s, the sandstone building stock of Scottish cities had been the focus of an active and widespread cleaning campaign. Unfortunately, many buildings had suffered damage because of injudicious or inappropriate cleaning methods, particularly chemical cleaning. Concerned about this damage, Historic Scotland (formerly HBMD) and the Scottish Development Agency (SDA), joint funders of cleaning and surface repair conservation schemes, commissioned a detailed research project into the effect of cleaning on Scottish sandstone buildings. The brief of the two-year project was to examine the general reasons for stone cleaning, to assess available cleaning methods, to assess the strength and weakness of stones used in Scottish buildings to various stone cleaning techniques, and to prepare a guide to assist those in the decision-making process of whether to clean or not.

The study was undertaken by the Masonry Conservation Research Group of the Robert Gordon Institute of Technology, at the University of Aberdeen (RGIT). In April 1992, a conference was held in Edinburgh to discuss the findings; these and the conference papers were published later that year.[3,4]

In many parts of the UK, the cleaning industry was subdued during the two-year study period as many projects were deferred pending the outcome of investigations. Editorials in the technical press went to the extent of recommending that no cleaning be undertaken throughout the UK until such time as the results were known, even though the study was restricted to the sandstones of Scotland and was not a complete study of the operation and effect of chemical cleaning.

Much of the information presented was not new to specialist practitioners and it was considered incomplete in scope. However, widespread publication and review in the technical and popular press of some findings led to a somewhat alarmist reaction to chemical cleaning generally. Importantly, though, the conference warned of the need to identify details of masonry substrates which are to be cleaned by chemical means. A practitioner's guide based on the findings of the Scotland study has also been published.[5]

During this period it was sad to see the many good cleaning projects which had been cleaned by chemical means receiving no acknowledgement. Because poor quality work had been done in certain quarters, many seemed to forget that this did not apply to every project, contractor or professional in the field. It needs to be remembered that many historic buildings and conservation areas have benefited from the effects of masonry cleaning. The experience of Glasgow is summarized in the following statement:

> Since the 1970s, we have been advising owners and professionals to consider well the risks *and* the benefits of stonecleaning, one at the same time. It is my considered opinion that as a whole, the stonecleaning programme has been highly successful in promoting the City's architecture as worthy of note (and therefore of care and

attention). Some of the problems we have inherited from a century or so of neglect and bad constructional practice have meant that an ideal solution is unattainable, no matter what we do or do not do. Equally, some of our approaches to some of our buildings have been shown to be ill-advised, in that with hindsight and increased knowledge we could have done the job better. I do not, however, apologise for having tried. The benefits to the City are all too clear to see.[6]

In the early 1970s the conservation, repair and cleaning of historic stone buildings in Glasgow's central area began in earnest. Almost universally, stone cleaning was undertaken as part of a larger stone repairs package. While the work may have benefited from the knowledge and skills available today, the city could not afford the luxury of sitting back for another decade or so – the massive problems of overall neglect, the lack of investment in building maintenance and the lack of appreciation of the city's architecture all needed to be tackled urgently. While there have indeed been poorer examples of cleaning, as well as better ones, to which it is felt many causes might be attributed, these are less fortunate cases and should not be regarded as the norm. The stone cleaning programme in Glasgow has generally been seen as a major success.

On buildings of high historic merit, the case for masonry cleaning is very different from that for urban regeneration and requires particular justification. In such contexts, the need for cleaning must be proved conclusively and involve the advice of experts of history, architecture and masonry.

1.3 WHY BUILDINGS ARE CLEANED

The decision to clean a building is frequently made on the grounds of aesthetics. It is generally considered that a cleaned building looks better and is a greater civic asset in its cleaned form. Not only does soiling obscure and distort the building's original appearance, its presence on the masonry surface may also be causing damage at an increasing rate to the substrate. Soiling crusts contain soluble salts which can be transported into the masonry pores during wetting and drying phases. Soiling crusts of this kind do not protect masonry but cause continuous damage if they are not removed. See Chapter 3 (this volume) for further discussion on the damaging effects of soiling. This strong technical argument for cleaning is frequently ignored in certain circles.

Figure 1.1 The former Parcels Office and Midland Station, Nottingham. Cleaning was undertaken as the first step in the revitalization of this building as part of a major law courts development. It had not been cleaned before. The building is viewed by all users of the exisstttting Nottingham railway.

In the UK, cleaning is rarely conducted on its own and is usually associated with maintenance and repair works on the facade. Research undertaken by Trudie Mansfield indicates that stone cleaning may have benefits to the owner other than purely aesthetic ones, and that the public will continue to remain intolerant of soiled buildings.[7,8] Motives for cleaning were confirmed in responses to questionnaires sent to stone cleaning companies within the UK in 1987 and 1991. These two surveys are looked at below.

The 1987 survey

The principal reasons for having a building cleaned, identified by building owners or those in charge of buildings in both private and public sectors, were as follows:[9]

    39% to improve appearance
    28% as an integral part of the scheduled maintenance programme
    15% to identify defective structures
     9% to increase trade
     6% to increase the value of the property
     3% to blend with a new building extension

Replies from cleaning specialists identified some different reasons from those given by the property owners:

    29% to protect the building fabric
    20% to improve appearance
    19% to increase property value
    11% to enable a detailed structural survey to be undertaken
     8% to increase trade
     2% to improve 'social' environment
     2% to deter vandalism and graffiti

The 1991 survey

The responses to a second questionnaire issued to cleaning contractors in 1991 had adjusted to:[10]

    42% to improve appearance
    27% restoration/identification of faults
    10% part of lease/refurbishment package
     6% to blend in with surrounds
     5% to decrease long-term maintenance costs

4% to increase the value of the property

4% to upgrade housing stock

2% an alternative to painting

In 1991, more than 60 per cent of respondents felt that the public sector's motives for cleaning were the same as the private sector's. Nearly 60 per cent of their work came from the private sector, with a common ratio of 80 : 20 private to public being quoted.

The importance of cleaning in assisting to prevent future deterioration of the masonry is one of the least understood aspects of masonry cleaning. The value of removing soiling deserves higher recognition in the battle between the philosophy/aesthetics and the technical need for cleaning that has been joined in the UK. The value and necessity for cleaning as part of a masonry repair programme also deserves renewed emphasis.

It is hard to find practical market evidence that the cleaning of an historic facade increases the building's financial value. Assessment of a property's value includes its condition and necessary remedial works that will be required to make this good. Cleaning is frequently a small proportion of the total necessary works and is therefore, on its own, not easily identified as a major factor affecting value. However, it is significant as part of the total remedial package, particularly as it is the aspect of work which probably has the most dramatic visual impact.[11]

1.4 THE UK DEBATE

In 1932, R.J. Schaffer, the stone specialist, wrote:

> From the artistic standpoint, it is difficult to believe that the architect who designs with due regard to effects of light and shade, and who selects his materials for their colour, 'character', or texture, can tolerate the presence of soot and grime which hide the beauties of his materials and obliterate the craftsmanship of his design.[12]

In 1992, Edinburgh architect, Dennis Rodwell, wrote:

> Much of the quality of historic buildings, both in design and construction, derives from the articulation of form and the intricacies of detail. Observation of these qualities is rendered difficult and sometimes impossible if the enriching effect of the passage of light and shade is suppressed by filth.[13]

> Dirt, irrespective of whether or not it is of itself harmful to their fabric, makes old buildings look uncared for and unvalued. It

symbolises neglect. It encourages the view that maintaining old buildings is an insurmountable problem, that they have a finite life, and that conservation is an anachronism. It is a passive form of vandalism, that inspires the active.[14]

In 1989, The Prince of Wales, wrote:

> The Houses of Parliament look particularly wonderful since they've been cleaned – you see the full glory of them now.[15]

The view of conservationists in the 1990s who are less convinced of the need and value of masonry cleaning is expounded by Emma Crawford.[16] Conservationists are questioning the frequency with which masonry cleaning is undertaken as part of a refurbishment or masonry repair programme. They question the incentive of funding bodies that require a building which looks as if it has had money spent on its restoration. Their concerns extend to the legislative framework in which cleaning takes place at present, which they feel is inadequate and does not regulate stone cleaning practitioners. The protection afforded by the listing of historical buildings is considered of theoretical value only in most instances. Their concerns are usually justified, particularly where the necessary investigations, assessments and trials are not undertaken properly.

The proposal to clean the Sir Walter Scott Monument in central Edinburgh drew much interest during the public enquiry held in 1992 and 1993. (At the time of writing the final deliberations of the enquiry have not been published.) The monument, which was erected between 1840 and 1844 to the design of George Meikle Kemp, has a soaring, tiered spire which is rich in ornate gothic detail. An article by Architectural Heritage of Scotland prior to the enquiry explains the opinions of those who do not recommend cleaning.

> The Monument is black in part because it is so close to the railway. Smoke from steam trains and diesel fumes are an irrefutable part of its past. The site was chosen in favour of one in Charlotte Square, so the colour bears testimony to the site where the building has existed. To clean would not only remove this historical evidence, but would involve conjecture as to the colour the Monument might have been if the air conditions had been different.[17]

As such, the process is in contravention of the Burra Charter of Australia, Article 3 of which states:

> Conservation is based upon respect for the existing fabric and should involve the least possible physical intervention. It should not distort the evidence provided by the fabric . . .

Only work which is known and understood to protect and preserve the Monument should be permitted to this structure of such immense architectural, historical and cultural significance.[18]

Historic buildings certainly require special consideration regarding any works undertaken on them, more so than buildings of lesser historical value which are also constructed of traditional masonry materials, although there are many requirements common to both when cleaning and surface repair are being considered. The cleaning of scheduled monuments and listed buildings in England is covered by legislation to a certain extent.

1.5 LISTED BUILDINGS AND SCHEDULED MONUMENTS

The English Parliament has enacted laws since 1882 to protect examples of historical development.

Scheduled monuments are of national importance and are scheduled under the Ancient Monuments and Archaeological Areas Act 1979. Scheduling means that the Secretary of State for the Environment becomes directly responsible for the protection of the monument and for ensuring that the treatment, repair or use is compatible with its preservation as a monument. Their cleaning requires Scheduled Monument Consent from the Secretary of State for which a detailed specification is necessary. The consent is required even if on-site trials are proposed.

Listed buildings are protected by an extension of planning control which is primarily the responsibility of local authorities.

Buildings are classified into three grades: Grade I, II* and II. Grade I buildings are those considered to be of exceptional interest and represent about one per cent of the listed buildings. Grade II* buildings are of special interest and considered to be worthy of preservation. Grade II buildings are: (1) All structures not classified as Grade I or Grade II* but which were built prior to 1700 and survive in anything like the original condition; (2) most buildings built between 1700 and 1840.

Within the main groups there are various subclassifications. These can be for architectural or planning reasons or illustrating aspects of social or economic history. Typical examples are industrial buildings, railway stations, schools, hospitals, theatres, town halls, markets, exchanges, almshouses, prisons and mills. Certain technological innovations can be listed, including the use of wrought and cast iron,

Figure 1.2 To many, the soiling of Lichfield and other cathedrals is an important representation of the historic value and character of these monuments. Decisions to clean follow investigations as to if, why and how this should be done. This level of questioning is also suited to less prominent masonry structures.

prefabrication and the early use of reinforced concrete. Such examples are often associated with famous people or events. Listed buildings are usually occupied. However, there is an overlap, and certain structures can be both listed and scheduled, e.g. barns, bridges, guildhalls and industrial structures.

It is an offence to demolish, alter or extend a listed building without consent. This includes non-listed buildings within conservation areas. Masonry cleaning is considered an alteration which materially affects the character of a listed building and as such requires local authority consent before it can be carried out. The discretion as to whether formal consent to cleaning needs to be made lies with each individual authority. There is no nationwide standardisation regarding information, trials, or specialist input which should accompany an application for cleaning and little agreement among local authorities as to whether consent should be granted. The local authority must, however, always be consulted beforehand.

The Society for the Protection of Ancient Buildings (SPAB) is a non-statutory body whose opinion regarding historical building repair is held in high regard. In his manifesto of 1877 for the foundation of the SPAB, William Morris explains how and why the society proposed to protect ancient buildings.

> Moreover, in the course of this double process of destruction and addition the whole surface of the buildings is necessarily tampered with; so that the appearance of antiquity is taken away from such old parts of the fabric as are left, and there is no laying to rest in the spectator the suspicion of what may have been lost; and in short, a feeble and lifeless forgery is the final result of all the wasted labour.[19]

The SPAB provides a valuable reminder that the original surface of stonework tells us much about the history of a structure and its removal with all associated honorable scars of age is considered incomprehensible from a philosophical point of view. The SPAB continues to advocate caution regarding historic masonry cleaning.

In its technical pamphlet on masonry cleaning, the SPAB presents a cautious attitude to cleaning and advises that the following stages should precede any cleaning contract:[20]

1. Decide whether cleaning is necessary and what it will achieve. The decision to clean the masonry of an historic building is extremely significant and should be weighed thoroughly.

   Before the decision to clean or not to clean is taken by

owners and their agents, regard should be had to the philosophical questions raised by the practice of cleaning and the practical questions of the potential for physical and/or chemical alteration of the masonry surfaces. The decision not to clean can, at times, be the correct decision and this option should always be considered.

2. On the basis of analysis and on-site trials, select a cleaning method appropriate to the substrate and to the degree of soiling.

3. Think through all the stages of the cleaning contract and ensure they are properly specified and costed.

4. Specify all the associated repair work likely to be necessary in the form of replacement of damaged elements or pointing of joints and determine what the sequence of work will be.

5. Select contractors with proven experience in the type of cleaning and repairs proposed and look at other work they have carried out.

The SPAB's view is considered conservative by many practitioners as it does not consider what the effect would be of not cleaning, in terms of appearance or the removal of soiling which is harming the substrate.

1.6 A BALANCED VIEW

We must be careful not to criticize cleaning jobs out of context. Many projects which we now consider to have been poorly executed and damaging were, at the time they were done and within the context of available skills and processes, considered to be very good. At the time it was done, the wet abrasive cleaning of unglazed terracotta of the Royal Albert Hall, so frequently cited now as an example of the damage of abrasive cleaning on terracotta, was considered a good cleaning job. The cleaning of major buildings such as these was not done without extensive trial periods and the preparation of documentation.

When buildings in urban England were cleaned for the first time, about sixty years ago, the thickness of the soiling made it virtually impossible to determine the extent and nature of deterioration and repair work. Most had over eighty years of encrusted soiling on them. In protected areas in urban environments, this was frequently 25–75 mm (1–3 in.) thick and completely hid the mouldings and other features on the undersides of cornices. Prior to cleaning it was impossible to see the masonry surface and its detail beneath. As a result, specialist contractors were frequently cleaning 'blind' and much damage was done, even by 'the experts'. Abrasive methods gave quick results then, as they do now, and a large proportion of blame for damage can be attributed to them. The methods and technology of the 1970s were relatively crude compared with today's, although in some quarters high quality cleaning of the heavy encrustations was achieved using misting sprays and other more controllable methods.

Then, as now, the full complexity of masonry, its soiling, and details of appropriate processes required to separate the two without damage are not understood on many cleaning projects. Few professionals understand the range of operations required on site to enable a cleaning specification to be carried out satisfactorily. Only a handful of practitioners have sufficient knowledge and experience to enable the full range of assessments, tests and documents to be undertaken properly. There remains a very low cost expectation for masonry cleaning which reflects the low priority it is often given.

1.7 INDIVIDUAL SOLUTIONS

The cleaning of masonry should remove the soiling and leave the stone intact and unaltered. The ideal would be a cleaning method which would operate selectively on the soiling alone. In reality, no such method exists but this should always be the aim of any cleaning operation. If it is in the best interest for a building surface to be cleaned, this must be done by the gentlest possible method which has been selected on the basis of the individual needs of the building.

Historic building materials are not indestructible. There is no one formula for the cleaning of historic building surfaces. It is even dangerous to suggest that there is a group of appropriate formulae. Each situation is different. There will, of course, be a thread of similarities from job to job, but if all the many details and permutations of each case are properly assessed, this must mean that the final procedures for one building's cleaning will be significantly different from those used on similar materials elsewhere.

1.8 REALISTIC EXPECTATIONS

Stone cleaning should never be expected to return a facade to its original colour or state. In the years since its erection, a building will have soiled, weathered, decayed and developed patinas on the stone surfaces, changing in many irreversible ways. The stone cleaning should not attempt to remove staining which has taken place as a result of mineralogical changes within the stone itself.

Stone cleaning will not be equally successful on all areas of a building. Flat, smooth ashlar is generally more successfully cleaned than sills, cornices, pinnacles and other protrusions. Unless surfaces are damaged or altered by a cleaning process, a range of degrees of cleaning must be expected. Some, such as that on carving, will be more visually acceptable than others but this is part of the reality of cleaning, particularly on sandstone surfaces.

The successful cleaning of an historic masonry facade requires several critical ingredients, including:

1. A good understanding of the facade's materials, their condition, the nature and effect of soiling on them.
2. Details of materials and procedures of appropriate cleaning methods.
3. A specification which defines as accurately as possible the materials and methods that will be required to clean the facade and which provides sufficient information to enable truly competitive tendering.
4. Undertaking of the work by an experienced contractor who has the capacity not only to undertake the work but also to deal with the many modifications of process that the facade will demand as its characteristics become better known.
5. The undertaking of the work by a contractor who is being paid to do the necessary works and is not in a contractual situation which will force short-cuts or a reduction in the standard of workmanship.

These matters are central to many of the discussions in the remaining chapters of these books.

1.9 THE NEED FOR MASONRY CLEANING

The need to remove soiling must always be investigated from two angles: aesthetics and the on-going well-being of the masonry beneath.

The aesthetics of soiling

All traditional building materials will weather and soil as the result of exposure to the environment. A building's soiling pattern will depend on its environment, orientation of the facades, properties and behaviour of the materials of which it is constructed and the interaction among these, rainwater run-off patterns and their relationship to the architecture of the building, the time which has lapsed since the building was last cleaned and the impact of any previous cleaning operation.

As a building weathers and soils, its appearance changes. Light, initial soiling will cause relatively subtle alterations to the building's appearance which are usually complimentary to the architecture beneath. Once the soiling level becomes moderate, detail, colour and texture of the surfaces beneath begin to be obscured and the pattern of soiling interacts with the architectural features, also adding its own pattern to the facade. The patterns of soiling may be unrelated to and visually distracting from the architectural features beneath. Once the soiling level becomes heavy, much of the facade is affected by a uniform darkening which obscures its architecture and any light and shadow effects.

The RGIT investigated the aesthetic basis for masonry cleaning and the assumption that all buildings are visually improved as a result of cleaning. The study aimed to discover when and how buildings are aesthetically improved by cleaning. It investigated the relationship between type of building, materials used in construction, aesthetic value, and whether the building would be aesthetically enhanced or deteriorate following cleaning.[21]

Based on responses to questionnaires conducted in Edinburgh and Glasgow, the study established an interesting relationship between the aesthetic value, soiling and visual complexity of a building. It was found that initially, after construction or cleaning, the building had a positive aesthetic value:

> After a number of years of weathering, where accumulations of dirt are consistent with the architectural features and the stone texture, complexity is increased and aesthetic value rises to a peak. Thereafter, it begins to decline as soiling increases, becoming unrelated to underlying architectural features. As soiling becomes increasingly heavy, complexity is reduced and aesthetic value decreases to a point where the whole facade is blackened and complexity is at a minimum.[22]

Figure 1.3 The level of resoiling adherent to surfaces of the Sir John Soane's Museum, 13 Lincoln's Inn Fields, London, prior to cleaning and surface repair works undertaken in 1992. Soiling patterns had begun to detract from the architecture. Incomplete removal of thick layers of oil-based paints to the incised decorations were also disfiguring and also needed to be removed. Stone corbel brackets, palmette blocks and the terracotta figurines were cleaned and repaired off-site by conservators as a separate contract. The remaining surfaces were cleaned by a specialist cleaning contractor.

From the findings, it was deduced that heavily soiled buildings were aesthetically less pleasing than when cleaned, and that old buildings with light soiling were aesthetically more pleasing than the same buildings without soiling. Findings supported the view that the removal of all soiling from historic buildings removes part of the sense of their history. The study found that buildings which were moderately soiled were viewed most favourably. The removal of heavy soiling was also viewed favourably, although the reaction to the lightly soiled cleaned building was less favourable.

Caution must be exercised when interpreting the above findings on sandstone buildings beyond the area of the study and certainly with regard to buildings of different masonry substrates altogether.

Technicalities of soiling: the health of the masonry beneath

There is a second, equally important side to the argument of whether a masonry surface should be cleaned or not, and that is the effect of soiling on the masonry beneath.

There is a technical, physical need for cleaning to ensure better health for the masonry beneath. The inherent colouring of masonry which it is desirable to retain must not be confused with the soiling which has been deposited by rain, wind, etc. Deposited soiling will contain soluble salts (pollutants) which can be transported into the pores and fissures of the stone during wetting and drying cycles where they will cause on-going deterioration. Alternatively, the soiling layer may act as a damp poultice of pollutants which will affect the masonry surface. The soluble salts in soiling do not protect masonry but cause it long-term damage if not removed.

Soiling deposits on stone usually consist of:

1. Mineral particles: soil, clay, lime, sand.
2. Industrial and household waste products: fly ash, combustion products, tar, carbon, mineral binding agents, oil and unburned diesel residues.
3. Animal and vegetable matter: pollen, algae, insects, bacteria.[23]

On limestones and marbles, thick, extensive deterioration is frequently found in association with thick deposits. The main components of these black crusts are gypsum and carbon particles. On sandstones,

Figure 1.4 The effect of weathering and atmospheric soiling on Portland limestone in central London.

bricks, terracotta and granite, carbon particles again feature prominently. In both instances, sulphates feature prominently as do soluble salts which can be deposited or originate from the masonry construction. The soiling needs to be removed to prevent damage by these. Further details on the effect of soiling and the need for its removal are found in Chapter 3 (this volume).

It must be the aim of everyone involved in the cleaning of historic masonry to develop and use safe and effective cleaning agents and techniques. Cleaning can be the most severe experience a masonry facade will be subject to in its life. It is the responsibility of clients, professionals, funding bodies and contractors to work together to ensure that a cleaning operation enhances the well-being of an historic building.

REFERENCES

1. Grimmer, A.E. (1979) *Dangers of Abrasive Cleaning to Historic Buildings: Preservation Brief 6*. Technical Preservation Services Division, Heritage Conservation and Recreation Service, Washington: US Government Printing Office, p.3.
2. Ashurst, J. and Dimes, F.G. (eds) (1990) *Conservation of Building and Decorative Stone*. London: Butterworth/Heinemann, Volume 2, p.125.
3. Robert Gordon Institute of Technology (Masonry Conservation Research Group) (1992) *Stone Cleaning in Scotland: Research Commission Investigating the Effects of Cleaning Sandstone*, Research Reports 1, 2 and 3, Research Summary, Literature Review. Historic Scotland, Scottish Enterprise, and Robert Gordon Institute of Technology.
4. Webster, R.G.M. (ed.) (1992) *Stone Cleaning and the Nature, Soiling and Decay Mechanisms of Stone*, Proceedings of the International Conference held in Edinburgh, UK, 14–16 April 1992. London: Donhead.
5. Robert Gordon Institute of Technology (1993), *Stone Cleaning: A Practitioner's Guide*. Historic Scotland, Scottish Enterprise, and Robert Gordon Institute of Technology.
6. Martin, D.T. (1992) *Stone Cleaning in Glasgow*, statement issued 15 April to International Conference on Stone Cleaning, Heriot-Watt University, Edinburgh.
7. Mansfield, T.A. (1988) Building soiling and the stone cleaning industry, *Stone Industries*, April, pp.24–26.
8. Mansfield, T.A. (1992) Sources of building soiling and a review of the stone cleaning industry 1991, *Stone Cleaning and the Nature, Soiling and Decay Mechanisms of Stone*, Proceedings of the International Conference held in Edinburgh, UK, 14–16 April 1992. London: Donhead, p.84.
9. Mansfield, T.A. (1988) op. cit., p.26.
10. Mansfield, T.A. (1992) op. cit., p.90.
11. Robert Gordon Institute of Technology (Masonry Conservation Research Group) (1992), op. cit., Research Report 3, p.76
12. Schaffer, R.J. (1932) *The Weathering of Natural Building Stones*, Building Research Special Report No.18, Department of Scientific and Industrial Research. London: HMSO, p.9.
13. Rodwell, D. (1992) Stone cleaning in urban conservation, *Stone Cleaning and the Nature, Soiling and Decay Mechanisms of Stone*, Proceedings of the International Conference held in Edinburgh, UK, 14–16 April 1992. London: Donhead, p.200.
14. Ibid., p.200.
15. Charles, Prince of Wales (1989) *Vision of Britain: A Personal View of Architecture*. London: Doubleday.
16. Andrew, C. and Crawford, E. (1992) Conservation and planning considerations in stone cleaning, *Stone Cleaning and the Nature, Soiling and Decay Mechanisms of Stone*, Proceedings of the International Conference held in Edinburgh, UK, 14–16 April 1992. London: Donhead, pp.193–198.
17. Crawford, E. (1992) Coming clean, *Context* No.35 (The Association of Conservation Officers), September, p.20.
18. Ibid., p.20.
19. Morris, W. (1877) *Manifesto for the Society for the Protection of Ancient Buildings*.

20. Ashurst, N. and J. (1991) *Cleaning Stone and Brick*, SPAB Technical Pamphlet 4. London: SPAB, p.2.
21. Robert Gordon Institute of Technology (Masonry Conservation Research Group) (1992) op. cit., Research Report 3.
22. Andrew, C. (1992) Towards an aesthetic theory of building soiling, *Stone Cleaning and the Nature, Soiling and Decay Mechanisms of Stone*, Proceedings of the International Conference held in Edinburgh, UK, 14–16 April 1992. London: Donhead, p.80.
23. Amoroso, G.G. and Fassina, V. (1983) *Stone Decay and Conservation: Atmospheric Pollution, Cleaning, Consolidation and Protection*, Materials and Science Monograph II. Amsterdam: Elsevier, p.256.

Chapter Two

Understanding Building Surfaces

Every masonry project requires an individually tailored cleaning process which takes due consideration of its particular requirements and controls the application of materials and methods. This chapter looks at the investigative processes that need to be undertaken, firstly, before the final decision to clean is made and, secondly, before the contract is let and work commences.

2.1 THE NECESSARY EXPERTISE

It is important that suitably qualified and experienced people are involved throughout the process. Cleaning buildings actually covers many processes, so in order to safeguard historic architecture against incorrect processes, and uninformed interventions, a thorough understanding of these processes, of building stones, and of the architecture involved must be demonstrated in the agent wishing to clean a building.[1]

Particular care must be taken with buildings of special architectural or historic interest. For listed buildings, the local planning authority should be asked whether listed building consent is needed for the cleaning or for on-site trials, as both can significantly alter the appearance of a building.

Written consent from the Secretary of State for these operations will certainly be required by owners of scheduled monuments (see Chapter 1 of this volume). Whether a building of traditional masonry materials is listed or scheduled or neither, it is always worth the investment of taking particular care in the design of its cleaning process as damage can be avoided and, often, money is not spent unnecessarily.

2.2 AESTHETIC AND TECHNICAL QUESTIONS

Prior to making the final decision to clean, the following technical and aesthetic questions should be answered satisfactorily.

Aesthetic considerations

1. Will cleaning enhance the appearance of the building?
2. How will the visual character of the building be changed as a result of the cleaning? What effect will the cleaning have on revealing the architecture and the weathered colour of the stone beneath?
3. Will the building still reflect its historical character?
4. What effect will the cleaning of the building have on the streetscape, the townscape or on the building setting?
5. How will the appearance of the cleaned building compare with uncleaned buildings adjacent?
6. If indent repairs, replacement and repointing are to be undertaken to the masonry, what will the building look like if it is not cleaned in association with these repairs?
7. What will be the visual effect of residual staining which will be revealed by the primary cleaning?
8. Does the whole of the building need to be cleaned or only parts and what will be the visual impact of this?
9. What degree of cleaning is to be achieved?

Technical considerations

1. What is the nature of the masonry?
2. What is the nature of the soiling on the masonry surface?
3. How has it affected the health of the masonry so far?
4. Are there certain areas where its effect has been especially damaging?

5. What will be the effect of removing the soiling on the future performance and health of the masonry?

6. What would be the effect of partial cleaning on the future performance and health of the stone?

7. What are the detailed constituents of the masonry?

8. How have the physical characteristics of the masonry been affected by the soiling?

9. What types and quantities of soluble salts are present on the soiled surface and at what depth?

10. What proportion of deterioration of the masonry can be attributed to the soiling and to the constituents and characteristics of the masonry?

11. What is the extent and colour of any inherent patina which has developed over the decades and should not be removed during cleaning?

12. How will the survey of each facade be undertaken and who has the necessary experience?

13. What sampling and analysis need to be undertaken to understand fully the masonry, its weathering and its soiling?

14. What surfaces of the masonry are sound, where are these located and what is their proportion compared with friable and delaminating surfaces?

15. What types of masonry surface are involved, i.e. plain ashlar, moulded cornices, carved sculptures, etc. and can due respect be given to each of these?

16. Who will co-ordinate and assess the on-site trials? Where will these be located, and which materials and processes will be included? What assessment procedures should be adopted before, during and after the trials?

17. What level of clean can be achieved safely?

18. Is partial cleaning recommended and a practical alternative?

19. What will be the interrelationship between the associated surfaces repairs that are required and the cleaning?

20. Are sufficient skills and finances available to undertake the selected cleaning process(es)?

2.3 CRITERIA FOR CLEANING TECHNIQUES

The following are essential criteria for any cleaning technique which is undergoing early consideration:

1. The technique must not cause direct or indirect harm to the building surfaces concerned.
2. The technique must allow the widest possible preservation of the masonry's patina (inherent colouring). With stone, this may alter in different environments and different locations.
3. The technique must not deposit or generate by-products which, remaining in these stones, may affect the future preservation (e.g. soluble salts). The technique must not initiate new decay processes or exacerbate old ones.
4. Use of the technique must be controllable in all aspects so that the operator can adjust and interrupt cleaning as necessary.

Cleaning methods must be determined for each individual case, especially where historic or artistic values are at stake.

2.4 THE NECESSARY INVESTIGATIONS

Prior to cleaning, the following investigations must be completed:

1. The masonry type(s), source and characteristics have been researched and are understood by those wishing to clean.
2. The building's construction technology is understood, particularly how moisture moves over and through the building, which has hugely significant implications for wet cleaning processes.
3. The soiling on a building or monument's surface has been properly and fully analysed.
4. The soiling has been proved to be damaging if left in place.
5. A cleaning method has been selected that can be proved to be less harmful to the stone in the longer term than allowing the soiling to remain in situ.
6. The operation will be carried out by adequately regulated contractors and trained operatives, to programmes in which the incentives of accelerated completion times have been addressed.
7. The operation will be adequately supervised by knowledgeable building professionals.
8. The planning authorities exercising controls on cleaning operations are in possession of or have access to such knowledge and are backed up by adequate detailed guidance to carry out the control processes.[2]

The evaluations necessary to answer the many questions posed must be undertaken by experienced individuals with specialist knowledge in the cleaning and surface repair of porous materials (stone, brick, terracotta, mortars and renders). These materials are easy to abuse if this understanding is not available.

The necessary assessments will involve:

STEP 1:   Inspection and identification:
                 ♦ Survey of the facades.
                 ♦ Analysis of substrates and soiling.
STEP 2:   On-site trial cleaning, including post-trial evaluation and analysis.
STEP 3:   Preparation of a specification setting out all aspects of the selected processes and necessary associated provisions.

2.5 SOILING AND WEATHERING

Historic buildings include a wide variety of natural and man-made materials which have experienced a similarly wide variety of weathering and soiling effects. There is no standard answer or standard specification for the cleaning of general categories of masonry substrate.

The weathering, deterioration and soiling of masonry are interrelated in an often complex process or manner. They all need to be understood before a cleaning programme is initiated. Problems with a cleaning project will occur in the short or long term where this is not the case.

The soiling and weathering of a building will depend on the material of which it is made, its geometry, exposure, orientation and details of its architecture. It is also necessary to understand the effects of microclimate and the wetting/drying, heating/cooling and freezing/thawing cycles to ensure all parts of the equation are properly assessed.

On sandstone facades, it is the features which are wet most and longest which soil most. 'Sandstone weathers dirty.'[3] Finials, parapets, copings, gargoyles, string courses, sills and buttresses are architectural features prone to total and frequent saturation and consequently, are the most heavily soiled. The increased number of wetting and drying cycles they experience lead initially to concentrated soiling and eventually to accelerated decay.

On a smaller scale, micro-climatic effects provide a range of soiling and deterioration patterns dictated primarily by orientation and prevailing weather conditions. On a similar scale, soiling patterns can

Figure 2.1 Soiling patterns are very informative regarding the condition of masonry. They should be studied on a small and large scale. A photographic record prepared prior to cleaning can be invaluable in understanding stains which may remain after cleaning.

be affected by differences in porosity on a stone by stone basis and within the same stone.

The evaluations must be undertaken by those who can 'read' masonry surfaces, assess the aesthetic, physical and chemical effects of cleaning trial work, balance and integrate the results of analytical work and combine practical considerations of the large-scale operation of cleaning methods to produce a detailed specification which clearly sets out for tendering contractors all details of the processes they are required to undertake. It should be remembered that manufacturers are in the business of selling their machinery or products, and masonry contractors are in the business of selling masonry cleaning and repair. Instances will occur when it is advisable to seek the services of an independent consultant, specialising in or having particular knowledge of historical masonry cleaning so that the requirements of the building receive prime consideration.

2.6 STEP 1: INSPECTION AND INDENTIFICATION – SURVEY OF THE FACADE

The facade should first be inspected at close range and each material identified. These could include limestone, sandstone, brickwork (various colours), terracotta (glazed or unglazed), tiles (glazed or encaustic), lime-based or cement-based mortars in joints or in previous repairs. During this assessment phase, the condition of the masonry, its joints and other associated materials should be evaluated. The types of soiling or staining should also be identified. The effect of previous cleaning and remedial works should also be assessed. It is important to determine whether superficial surface treatments have been applied at some time in the past.

Identification of substrate

A description of the properties and characteristics of sandstones, limestones, bricks, terracotta/faience, mortars and renders is provided in Chapter 3, (this volume).

It is essential that all masonry materials of which a facade is composed are identified. When heavily soiled, some materials can be difficult to identify. It used to be considered sufficient to identify masonry materials as acid-resistant or acid-soluble. Acid-resistant materials were deemed to include granite, most sandstones and the fired clay products (brick, terracotta, tiles). Acid-soluble materials, those comprising principally calcium carbonate, included limestones, marble, travertine, calcareous sandstone, lime-rich mortars, gypsum and lime-based plasters. All are readily dissolved by concentrated acid-cleaning solutions. If it was not possible to identify a facade material visually, a drop of 3–5% HCl (hydrochloric acid) solution was placed on the exposed masonry surface. If the substrate was acid-soluble the stone beneath the drop reacted with a 'fizz', indicating that it was acid-sensitive. On acid-resistant surfaces the drop of weak acid had little or no reaction.

However, this basic level of identification has proved insufficient, particularly regarding chemical cleaning of sandstones which may have a calcareous component reduced or removed from the surface layers by weathering and/or pollution. In addition, Dolomitic limestones will show little reaction to hydrochloric acid but will respond adversely to cleaning acids generally used.

Figure 2.2 Although The Monument is composed solely of Portland limestone, the different surface types (carved, lettered, intricately moulded, fluted and plain) mean that modifications in the selected cleaning method will need to be included for each of these. The cleaning of the figured panel is the realm of a stone conservator.

Figure 2.3 The assessment of brickwork must always include consideration of the condition of joints and the constituents and characteristics of the mortar. In this instance, the original sand/lime mortar had weathered back from its original profile and its outer layer was very soft. On the whole, the wall did not need repointing. It would have if excessively high rinse pressures had been used to remove chemical cleaning products. Cleaning of this wall also needed to respect the soft, textured nature of the eighteenth-century bricks and the many variations in hardness that could be found on a brick-by-brick basis and within individual bricks.

The extent of cleaning and repair works can change dramatically from that assessed from a ground level inspection to actual work on site. Essential information from these areas can only be successfully gained from a mobile platform which enables close range inspection, particularly of the upper, more heavily weathered reaches of a facade.

Figure 2.4 Masonry surfaces often contain areas which are firm and sound and areas which are weathered. The selected cleaning process must serve both situations. In this situation, rinse pressures suitable for sound surfaces had to be greatly reduced to minimize losses to the intermixed areas of granulation and delamination.

The hire of a platform for a day is always worthwhile when the benefits of the information gained are assessed.

The cleaning of a facade is often considered the first step in a conservation/repair programme, as once a facade is cleaned the true condition of its masonry is more readily and fully appreciated. Having said this, a soiled facade provides extensive information about its condition and it can be possible to establish some of the details of a masonry repair programme prior to cleaning. The weathering and soiling patterns on facades provide important information as to the breakdown of various areas of the masonry.

Figure 2.5 Where the sandstone to this Birmingham church has not been protected from the full effects of weathering, it has undergone colour changes which originate from constituents within the stone. Petrographic analysis would have identified colour changes to the outer zone of the stone before cleaning of its intensely blackened surfaces began. In the position where the memorial was fixed, the colour of the stone when the church was erected can be seen.

Cleaning is generally completed before the undertaking of repairs, but certain works, e.g. temporary joint filling, repointing or the removal of loose fragments of deteriorated surfaces may need to be done beforehand. The extent and need for protective measures to the masonry and its openings, at times a considerable cost factor within a masonry cleaning programme, should be also identified.

The surface form and finish of masonry units must be respected at all times. Window tracery, ornate mouldings, vermiculated blocks, pilaster and column capitals all have intricate and complex surfaces which frequently require different approaches to cleaning from those for surrounding ashlar. Original finishes to masonry units, however subtle, must also be retained.

While certain cleaning materials and methods are more suitable to certain types of masonry material, the details of the manner in which they are used in each individual case must be determined. There will be instances where certain cleaning and methods will be inappropriate and can therefore be ruled out at an early stage. Hydrofluoric acid-based cleaners should not be used on polished granite, glazed surfaces, limestone or marble and their use on calcareous sandstones must be carefully controlled. Abrasive cleaning methods are not suited to polished surfaces of any kind, to unglazed terracotta and must be used with extreme caution on intricately carved or moulded surfaces. Granulating or delaminating surfaces of any stone can be more susceptible to retention of chemicals and damage by abrasive or water impact than sound surfaces adjacent to them. At an early stage it will be obvious that these areas will require a modified cleaning approach. With all chemical cleaning methods, penetration of defective joints and the potential for deposition of chemical must be guarded against. Open and defective joints can also be problematic with water-based cleaning methods, including wet abrasive.

On completion of these preliminary investigations, it should be possible to anticipate the effect of a cleaning programme in terms of associated remedial works, the final visual result and the complexity of the cleaning procedures. A photographic record of the building in its untreated state should be made.

Questions to be answered by the survey

1. Of what masonry and non-masonry materials is the building constructed? What types of surface are present? Smooth, granulating, delaminating, rock-faced, carved, moulded, etc.
2. In what condition are the elements, individually and the facade and building as a whole?
3. In what condition is the pointing and how has this weathered in relation to the associated masonry materials?
4. Has there been any interactive weathering among the materials used?

5. Has the building been cleaned before and if so, how?
6. What have been the effects of this cleaning?
7. Have any surface treatments been applied?
8. Has weathering caused staining to the masonry which will be revealed during the cleaning?
9. What degrees of atmospheric soiling are present? What range of cleaning techniques will be necessary to address these?
10. Once it has been cleaned, what will the building look like as it gradually resoils?
11. What associated remedial works will be required?
12. What limitations do the remedial works impose on the proposed cleaning?
13. What is the nature of the soiling and what is its effect on the masonry surfaces?
14. What effect will its removal have on the durability of the masonry?
15. What will happen to the masonry if the soiling is not removed?
16. What materials and methods should be used to clean the various masonry surfaces?
17. What remedial work such as joint filling should be undertaken prior to the cleaning contract?
18. What analysis on the masonry and soiling needs to be undertaken? What locations should the samples be taken from, by whom and by which techniques? (Analysis is discussed later in this chapter.) It may be necessary to take discrete chips or dry cores for quantitative analysis of soluble salts on the surface and at depth, petrographic identification of stone constituents and decay processes which may involve the use of scanning electron microscopy and the determination of porosity and/or water absorbency.

Many questions relating to operational aspects of the procedure must also be answered as they all have significant cost implications:

1. How are windows and other openings to be protected?
2. How are painted or polished surfaces to be protected? Thorough protection of openings is a time-consuming exercise which must be clearly identified as an important aspect of work within the contract documents, to ensure it is not skimped on.

3. What types of scaffolding/sheeting are required: width of scaffold, fully boarded, fully sheeted with what type of sheeting, capping of tubes?
4. How will the cleaning operation affect the owner, occupants and users of the building, and how has negative impact been minimized?
5. What are the requirements of the relevant authorities and how have these been incorporated: Health and Safety at Work Act, local planning authority, police, COSHH (Control of Substances Hazardous to Health Regulations, 1988)?
6. How will cleaning be phased into other works? Will it be possible to undertake it in a continuous operation?

The survey process should also involve the undertaking of on-site trials prior to finalizing of the specification.

2.7 STEP 2: ON-SITE TRIAL CLEANING

Based on the findings of the preliminary investigations and any essential analysis, a series of on-site tests aimed at determining the most effective cleaning process should be undertaken. The need for thorough pretesting of all proposed cleaning methods and materials cannot be overemphasized. While experience is valuable, it should not be assumed that performance of one system in another context will prove similarly effective in the project to hand.

Analysis is particularly important when sandstone surfaces are to be cleaned as the binding materials of some are susceptible to certain cleaning methods. This must be known before trials are commenced.

The testing programme should be co-ordinated by the persons in charge of the cleaning project and should be designed to arrive at the gentlest, mildest, non-damaging, practical cleaning materials and methods capable of producing the desired degree of cleaning.

The number and size of the test panels should be determined by the architect or experienced professionals overseeing the inspection, testing and specification processes. The tests should be conducted in unobtrusive locations, on representative staining conditions. All types of masonry to be cleaned should be included.

As many stones with differing individual properties should be included. Several test areas may need to be undertaken to fulfil this. No test panel should be cleaned over during the general works, and their

Figure 2.6 On-site cleaning trials should be undertaken on panels of masonry at least 1 m² (4 ft × 4 ft) located as discreetly as possible. Areas of heavy and tenacious soiling should be included. In the situation shown, materials and processes which proved successful on ashlar have not been as successful on the more heavily soiled stone of the sill and plinth. Alternative methods have begun to be investigated in the spot trials on the second sill. All works conducted during on-site trials should be documented. On-site trials should always employ full scale procedures as would be adopted during the main contract. A small section of scaffold will be required to reach different soiling and masonry conditions at upper levels. There is frequently advantage in undertaking trials separately from and independent to the main contract.

location should therefore be clearly marked. In most instances, areas of 0.5–1 m² will need to be undertaken for meaningful results to be obtained.

It is important that trial cleaning areas should not be located on prominent parts of the building as the decision may be made not to clean. Part of the trial cleaning phase is necessarily experimental so the work is best undertaken on less important areas of masonry.

Ideally, the trials should include difficult areas of masonry such as the undersides of moulded or dentilled cornices where soiling encrustations are likely to be heaviest and masonry surface conditions are often delicate. Access is not always available to such heights at pre-contract stage, though. If trials are to be undertaken at or near ground level, it is essential that they include not only ashlar but also more heavily soiled areas such as moulded plinth blocks, window sills and ashlar beneath sills.

The testing should employ the same materials, equipment and procedures as proposed for the large-scale cleaning process. Ideally, the same personnel should be involved as there is much benefit to be gained from this continuity. The effect of the cleaning processes and any side-effects such as rinse waters on surrounding and adjacent masonry and non-masonry surfaces should be assessed.

The tests should include removal of atmospheric soiling, paint coatings, metallic stains and other selective soiling such as anti-pigeon gel. Any coating removal trials should be undertaken on the area where the layers are thickest.

The presence of a water repellent coating can impair the effectiveness of chemical cleaning products. The coating's removal will most likely require an additional cleaning process.

The test panels should be evaluated over a period of several days. They should be viewed when dry and when wetted by rain. The longer that trial cleaning areas can be left before evaluation, the better, as some effects stimulated by the cleaning processes, such as staining and efflorescence, become apparent only after the surface has dried out and stabilized with its environment. The development of salt efflorescences, algal growth, resoiling and colour changes may take up to twelve months to be noticeable, although sound assessments can usually be made within three to six weeks.

The test areas should require the architect's approval prior to undertaking further work. The client's agreement in writing should also be obtained. Successfully cleaned areas should be retained as reference points for the standard of clean required elsewhere on the building. This is of value from the client's and architect's point of view as the standard of clean required is determined, and from the contractor's point of view as the standard of clean expected is identified.

The trial cleaning phase will establish details of materials and methods which are appropriate on the areas of masonry on which the trials are conducted: they are not always fully indicative of the procedures that will be required on the full extent of masonry. It must be anticipated that adjustments will need to be made to the specified procedure to incorporate the demands of different areas of the masonry surfaces. The need for such adjustments is best determined at the beginning of the cleaning contract and may be determined on the basis of an additional series of trials undertaken by the contractor on the range of surface materials, types and soiling. Details of any such requirements should be set out in the specification.

Integrated analysis

The matter of the analysis of masonry surfaces before, during and after chemical cleaning is foremost in the mind of many professionals throughout the UK. Bad experiences have led to a desire for a conclusive, analytical process which can be undertaken in conjunction with cleaning trials and chemical cleaning projects. Only a very few professionals are experienced in the commissioning and interpretation of the appropriate testing. Scientific reports associated with cleaning programmes must establish details of the masonry constituents and the adherent soiling and investigate the effect of the selected method on the substrate. Results are of little value unless the correct tests have been undertaken and the full implications of the results are understood by the prime decision-maker. Not all testing houses have sufficient under-standing of masonry to be sufficiently positive in their recommen-dations. Unless they have been involved in the sample testing, they will have no knowledge of the building in question. For details of analysis recommended during and after cleaning, see Sections 2.11 and 2.12 of this chapter.

2.8 STEP 3: SPECIFICATION

Once the testing and analysis programme has been carried out and evaluated, a specification which defines the scope of works of the cleaning programme can be prepared. This document is essential for accurate cost estimates and truly competitive tendering. However, it should not remove the right to select a contractor on a basis other than cost. A specification for related temporary and permanent surface repairs should also be prepared in conjunction.

A specification should be as precise as possible concerning the extent of work, materials and methods to be used and all associated works required before, during and after the cleaning. General terms such as 'rake out and repoint as necessary' must be avoided if financial control and quality of work are to be maintained.

There needs to be a balance between technically accurate require-ments which include tight controls while almost eliminating margins for adjustment and clauses which allow for the capabilities of those professional cleaning firms which have valuable experience in the practicalities of executing quality work. Professionals are advised not to specify unreasonable levels of achievement or results and processes which are beyond their experience.

The specification needs to establish awareness of the relative delicacy of historic building fabric. Historic building fabric differs in many ways from modern construction materials. It is of particular importance that operatives and supervisors know when the limit which defines damage or over-cleaning is beginning to be approached and modifications in technique are required.

There is no substitute for correct diagnosis of the condition of masonry and a good, practical specification which sets out types and scopes of work. It enables the contractor to undertake the job properly and to engage the right people to do it. The specification must be a usable and understandable document which identifies everything that needs to be undertaken or provided and, therefore, costed.

Sources of advice

Architects, surveyors and other professionals who ask a cleaning contractor to advise them on a specification and to prepare a quotation based on these recommendations must be aware that the option put forward may not necessarily be the most appropriate but may be one which is of greatest benefit to the contractor. A client whose main requirement is to have his building cleaned at the lowest possible cost must recognize the probability for the selected system to damage the masonry surface and provide a visually unsatisfactory level of clean.

The UK Stone Federation has a stone cleaning division. The federation's membership comprises masonry repair and cleaning contractors who are interested in promoting high work standards in the cleaning industry nationwide. Advice from this body will stem from this experience.

BS 6270, Part 1, 1982 (plus amendments) covers the cleaning and surface repair of natural stone, carved stone, clay and calcium silicate brickwork, terracotta and faience. As stated in its foreword, in view of the widely differing ages, materials and locations of masonry buildings, BS 6270 gives only general guidance to enable the user to select the most appropriate method for the particular building concerned. The process of rewriting the standard began in 1993.

Even in its updated form, BS 6270 will not be a substitute for the informed assessment of masonry surfaces and the detailed determination of appropriate cleaning and surface repair procedures. In the light of the widespread misuse of the document in this regard, it is hoped that the new text outlines the procedure for selecting the correct cleaning process. Many professionals, owners and contractors rely heavily on what is, on its own admission, a general guidance document. The clause 'undertake cleaning in accordance with BS 6270', is virtually meaningless and a reflection on the abilities of the user. Even in its 1982 format the standard nevertheless establishes important principles and provides a good initial understanding of the considerations involved and potential for damage in the cleaning of historic masonry.

Specification outline

A specification for masonry cleaning on an historic facade should, as a minimum, address the following items:

1. General requirements
    Extent of work.
    Materials on the facade and site constraints.
    Historic value of the building.
2. Standard of clean to be obtained
    Outline of cleaning procedures.
    Test areas to be conducted by contractor.
3. Materials and processes for masonry cleaning
    Availability of materials.
    Manufacturer's recommendations and special requirements.
    Chemical cleaning materials (description).
    Abrasive cleaning materials (description).
    Materials and equipment for other processes (description).
    Product data sheets of cleaning materials.
    Delivery, storage and handling.
4. Compliance with regulatory requirements
    Health and Safety at Work Act, 1974.
    COSHH regulations.
    The cleaning contractor's health and safety policy.
    COSHH assessments and method statement.
    Local authority requirements.
    Noise.
    Environmental control.

Disposal of residues.
Police requirements.
Pedestrian access.
Access to building.

5. Scaffold
    Approvals, maintenance.
    Securing, bracing, capping of poles, ladder access, type of
        sheeting, width of boarding, extent of boarding out,
        toe boards, overall dimensions.

6. Protection
    Protection of other masonry or associated materials.
    Windows and openings.
    Dissimilar and incompatible materials.
    Fixtures and pavement installations.
    Controlling overspray.

7. Operatives and supervision
    Operatives (experience and continuity on site).
    Supervision (experience and continuity on site).
    Use of subcontractors.
    Specialist advice.
    Test reports (the use of alternative materials).
    Analysis and monitoring of cleaning procedures.

8. Equipment
    Details of capabilities required from:
        Pressure washers.
        Abrasive cleaning equipment, including nozzles.
    Equipment for the application and removal of chemical
        cleaning products.
    Equipment which is not permitted.

9. Environmental requirements
    Acceptable environmental conditions for the cleaning
        processes.
    Disposal of run-off and other wastes and residues.

10. Cleaning procedures
    Procedure for modification of the specification.
    Nebulous spray washing:
        Surface preparation.
        Nozzle types and sizes.
        Water flow rate.
        Measurement of water flow.
        Timing of intermittent sprays.

Use of associated methods and equipment.
Wet abrasive cleaning:
    Surface preparation.
    Acceptable wet abrasive pressures, abrasive type, size,
        etc.
    Work distances.
    Protection of adjacent surfaces.
Chemical cleaning procedures:
    Acceptable maximum water pressures.
    Pre-wetting.
    Methods of application, dwell times.
    Rinsing down prior to cleaning.
    Rinsing down (removing chemical).
    Dealing with efflorescence.
    pH testing of surfaces and other associated analysis.
Poultice/pack cleaning:
    Surface preparation.
    Poultice medium.
    Preparation/mixing of poultice.
    Method of application.
    Thickness of poultice.
    Covering, protection.
    Removal methods.
    Disposal of spent poultice.
    Neutralization (if any).
    pH testing of surfaces and other associated analysis.
Iron and copper stain removal:
    Product or process.
    Methods of application.
    Dwell time.
    Monitoring effects produced.
    Number of applications.
    Methods of removal.
    pH testing of surfaces and other associated analysis.
Paint removal:
    Surface preparation.
    Product or process.
    Number of applications.
    Methods of removal.
    pH testing of surfaces and other associated analysis.
Graffiti removal:

Surface preparation.
Product or process.
Number of applications.
Methods of removal.
pH testing of surfaces and other associated analysis.
Cement splash removal:
Surface preparation.
Product or process.
Number of applications.
Methods of removal.
pH testing of surfaces and other associated analysis.
Bird gel removal:
Surface preparation.
Product or process.
Number of applications.
Methods of removal.
pH testing of surfaces and other associated analysis.
11. Completion, final cleaning, final rinse down.

2.9 ROLE OF ANALYSIS

Discussion regarding the need for analytical investigation of masonry as part of the process of deciding whether to clean or not usually surrounds structures built of sandstone. The need for analysis in respect of limestone and marble masonry, fired clay products (brick and terracotta), etc. is equally valid.

Analysis provides a microscopic view of the materials to be cleaned, their constituents, details as to their condition and the reasons for their deterioration and breakdown. Visual inspection is rarely sufficient for a full understanding of what is going on. Many masonry cleaning disasters could have been avoided if the level of understanding provided by analysis had been available.

As the stone cleaning industry in the UK becomes increasingly sophisticated and therefore aware of the effects of malpractice, the role of analysis in the understanding of the detailed characteristics of the surfaces to be cleaned increases. This is particularly relevant regarding sandstones which have such a wide range of properties and characteristics.

Analysis has a role before cleaning, immediately after cleaning and subsequent to the cleaning to monitor the longer-term effects of the

Figure 2.7 Samples of stone for laboratory analysis can often be small and taken from discreet locations within areas of breakdown. The location and condition of masonry within a sample area must always be recorded so that the context of the sample is fully understood.

operation. It is of particular relevance with regard to chemical cleaning processes which operate on the basis of chemical reactions between the applied product, the soiling and the masonry. The analysis should investigate whether undesirable reactions have been avoided.

Analysis is necessary to confirm that precautionary procedures within the cleaning process have been undertaken correctly, that residues have not been left within the masonry and that unwanted reactions have not taken place. As a minimum, pH testing of all surfaces on which chemical cleaners have been used to remove soiling, stains or coatings should be undertaken. All stones should be investigated by petrographic analysis so that their properties and constituents are known and any susceptibility to particular cleaning processes are identified.

The scale (and cost) of analysis will depend on the extent of information required. Certain projects will demand a detailed programme. Even when this cannot be afforded, selected tests can be immensely useful and may prevent a cleaning disaster. It is not possible to list the requirements of a typical analysis programme, but this can be gleaned from the information which follows in this chapter and which discusses the principles of the various suitable testing methods. Case studies at the end of the volume describe instances in which these have been applied.

2.10 TEST METHODS

Identification and quantification of soluble salts

Test methods in this category are aimed at determining the type and quantity of soluble salts present in the masonry. This testing is particularly valuable when chemical cleaning is undertaken as it can be clearly established whether the chemicals have left any residues, be they soluble or insoluble.

It is usually necessary to take measurements within the surface (up to 6 mm) and then at increasing depths of 6 mm, to a full depth of 30 mm (four measurements). As a minimum, one surface measurement and another at approximately 18 mm may suffice. The salts are extracted with distilled water from powdered stone which has been removed in one of two ways:

1. From a core of stone removed by dry cutting methods. Wet core drilling will redistribute the existing salts which can lead to confused test results.
2. From stone powder removed from the wall by drilling. Flat headed drill bits are used to drill to the required depths and the resultant powder collected in sealable sample bags. More than one drill hole in the same location may be necessary to obtain the necessary quantity of powder. Ten grams minimum is required per test area.

The main analytical methods used are inductively coupled plasma emission spectrometry (ICP), atomic absorption spectrophotometry and ion chromatography (IC).

If the testing is being done in association with chemical cleaning, the analysis should be undertaken after trials and search for any ions which are contained in chemical cleaning agents, e.g. sodium (Na^+, from alkaline cleaners based on sodium hydroxide, $NaOH$), fluorine (F^-, from cleaners containing hydrofluoric acid, HF) and phosphate (PO_4^{3-}), from cleaners which contain orthophosphoric acid, H_3PO_4). Usually a much wider suite of ions will be identified and will include sulphate (SO_4^{2-}), a common constituent of most masonry soiling which may be transferred during a chemical cleaning operation. This latter information will be particularly relevant to the on-going deterioration of the cleaned surface.

Comparative soluble salts analysis is essential before and after chemical cleaning if the source of any emergent or subsurface salts is to be correctly attributed. Many wall materials will have an inherent salt loading which can be activated by water saturation alone.

It is possible to do chemical analysis of efflorescences, soluble salts which have crystallized on the masonry surface. This is usually done by X-ray diffraction (XRD). Test kits available for the measurement of the most common ions will give qualitative or semi-quantitative results. On-site readings can only be obtained for surface conditions. Measurement of ions at depth will require the taking and preparation of samples.

pH Measurement

The pH of samples is usually determined as part of the chemical aspect of analysis so that the acidicity or alkalinity of the masonry is known. These measurements assist the interpretation of other analytical results and provide information regarding cleaning product residues.

When chemical trials have been conducted, the completed panels should be monitored for alkaline or acidic cleaning residues. The measurement of the pH of rinse waters is one relatively simple and informative way of on-site checking for surface residues. pH test papers are readily available from suppliers of laboratory equipment in pH ranges of 0–14 and several smaller gradations of more limited ranges. pH 0–14 strips will indicate the approximate pH of a surface. Strips with smaller gradations will be required for a more accurate determination. Four-colour strips are preferable. Portable pH meters can be used but their measuring head cannot always be brought into contact with the masonry surface. Run-off needs to be collected and then measured. The use of pH strips is a basic method of identification which will provide information about the masonry surface but not about the material at depth.

The pH of a stone surface should not be assumed but should be tested before cleaning trials begin. The pH of the water used in the trials should also be tested beforehand. A surface which is tested immediately following chemical cleaning and rinsing should be retested 5–10 minutes later to confirm the initial result. By this time, further cleaning agent may have emerged and require further rinsing. Water is an efficient diluting and rinsing agent, but its use must be balanced with the risk of oversaturating the wall.

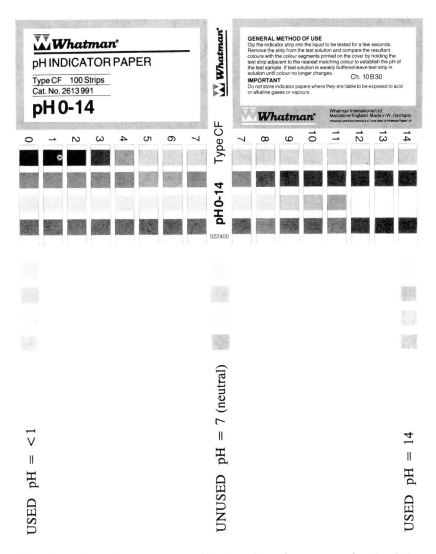

Figure 2.8 pH test strips are easy to use and give immediate information regarding the relative acidity or alkalinity of a masonry surface. Markers on the strips change colour in response to the pH of moisture on the surface. These are quickly matched with those on the chart. Alternatively, run-off can be collected in a small container and pH measured with a probe.

Microscopy

Petrographic analysis (stone constituents and properties)

Petrographic inspection of stone thin sections is one of the quickest and most cost effective means of obtaining a basic understanding of the mineralogy and chemistry of a stone sample. It is particularly good at revealing the intimate filling of voids by surface soiling.

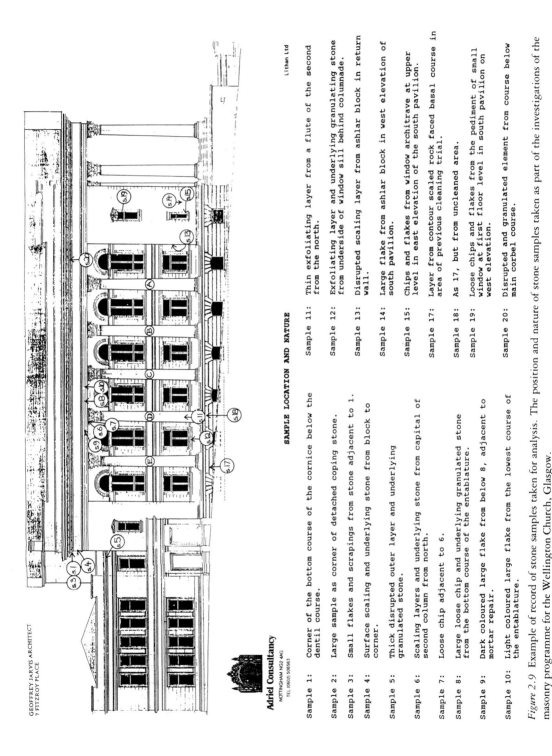

GEOFFREY JARVIS ARCHITECT
7 FITZROY PLACE

Adriel Consultancy
NOTTINGHAM NG2 4AG
TEL (0602) 508563

Lithan Ltd

SAMPLE LOCATION AND NATURE

Sample 1: Corner of the bottom course of the cornice below the dentil course.

Sample 2: Large sample as corner of detached coping stone.

Sample 3: Small flakes and scrapings from stone adjacent to 1.

Sample 4: Surface scaling and underlying stone from block to corner.

Sample 5: Thick disrupted outer layer and underlying granulated stone.

Sample 6: Scaling layers and underlying stone from capital of second column from north.

Sample 7: Loose chip adjacent to 6.

Sample 8: Large loose chip and underlying granulated stone from the bottom course of the entablature.

Sample 9: Dark coloured large flake from below 8, adjacent to mortar repair.

Sample 10: Light coloured large flake from the lowest course of the entablature.

Sample 11: Thin exfoliating layer from a flute of the second from the north.

Sample 12: Exfoliating layer and underlying granulating stone from underside of window sill behind columnnade.

Sample 13: Disrupted scaling layer from ashlar block in return wall.

Sample 14: Large flake from ashlar block in west elevation of south pavilion.

Sample 15: Chips and flakes from window architrave at upper level in east elevation of the south pavilion.

Sample 17: Layer from contour scaled rock faced basal course in area of previous cleaning trial.

Sample 18: As 17, but from uncleaned area.

Sample 19: Loose chips and flakes from the pediment of small window at first floor level in south pavilion on west elevation.

Sample 20: Disrupted and granulated element from course below main corbel course.

Figure 2.9 Example of record of stone samples taken for analysis. The position and nature of stone samples taken as part of the investigations of the masonry programme for the Wellington Church, Glasgow.

The stone sample is first impregnated with a resin which fills the pore spaces. A very thin slice of stone is then mounted on a glass slide, polished to a uniform standard thickness and examined under an optical polarized light microscope at high magnifications. The thin section is usually taken perpendicular to the surface so that the depth of the soiling, its interrelationship with the stone surface and any alterations which have taken place in the outer zone of the stone can be observed. Thin sections can be taken at any angle. Petrographic thin sections reveal the mineralogy, including the cementing materials and textures. Constituents which are potentially susceptible to chemical and abrasive cleaning can be identified.

Depletions of binder and alterations of mineral constituents which are due to natural weathering processes can be identified. It is important that this be done prior to chemical cleaning trials. Comparison with a thin section of cleaned stone would confirm whether the cleaning or weathering had caused these adjustments. Sampling after cleaning alone might lead to an incorrect conclusion.

Petrographic thin sections are also valuable before and after abrasive cleaning. When soiled stone in a thin section is viewed at magnification, it is easy to appreciate how difficult it is to clean stone completely by abrasive methods. Unless a significant layer of stone is removed, its pores will remain full of soiling, even though the surface soiling has been removed.

The area sampled depends on the size of section made and the area observed on the magnification used. Thin section work is usually carried out in the magnification range $\times 40$ to $\times 400$. At $\times 40$ the section area viewed is approximately 7 mm^2.

Other microscopic techniques

The surface of masonry can be viewed in three dimensions at magnification under a scanning electron microscope (SEM). It is possible to analyse the chemical elements on the surface by either SEM with X-ray facility or electron probe micro analysis (EPMA).

Samples of stone need to be removed from the building. It is therefore not practical to inspect large areas of the same surface before and after cleaning. Important information can be gleaned from SEM inspection of small-scale pieces before and after cleaning. The scanning electron microscope is nevertheless very useful for identifying microscopic surface changes. The area observed depends on the magnification used. SEM examination of rocks is usually carried out in the range of $\times 10$ to

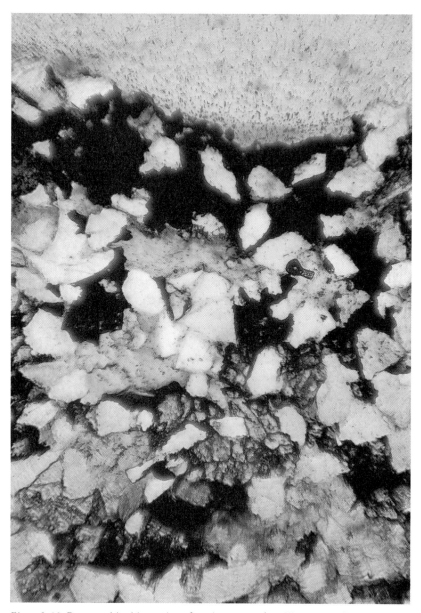

Figure 2.10 Petrographic thin section of a calcareous and argillaceous sandstone showing depletion of calcite from the outer area of the exfoliation flake and partial replacement by soiling. The increased porosity in the layer immediately beneath the outer surface is an imposed plane of weakness. (Photographed at ×60, plain polarized light, Lithan Ltd.)

×20,000. At ×10, the area viewed is approximately 100 mm² (10 mm × 10 mm).

SEM and petrographic thin sections are complementary, not mutually exclusive, procedures. SEM is more expensive, hence the more widespread use of thin sections. Thin sections enable subsurface layers to be investigated more readily than does SEM.

Field microscopes

Portable, hand-held field microscopes which provide magnifications of ×30 are useful investigative and diagnostic tools for assessing the relationship between soiling and the masonry beneath, and for establishing the effects of chemical and abrasive cleaning. Stone grains and the cementing material between are clearly visible at this magnification. On flat or fairly flat areas, it is possible to see residual soiling between grains and to clarify any confusion between stone patina and inherent staining.

Field microscopes are up to nine inches long and readily portable. Some have battery operated lights. They are available from select photographic shops and geologist suppliers.

Determining porosity and capillarity

Put simply, porosity is the amount of empty space in a piece of a particular stone. A stone is said to be permeable if a fluid moves easily through it. (Porosity and permeability are not necessarily related.) Capillarity is the degree to which a capillary network is responsible for the uptake and transport of water. (The capillary network comprises the microporosity which is usually taken as less than 2–5 microns diameter.)[4]

Porosity and capillarity are the properties which determine the capability of masonry to take up water, and the rate of its retention and loss. Traditional masonry materials are porous to varying degrees depending on their individual characteristics. They have the ability to take in moisture and need to be able to lose this freely. Surface deposits, including soiling, which inhibit this can lead to accelerated decay.

Mercury porosimetry establishes the porosity profile of a stone, i.e. the proportion of smaller voids to larger voids. Stone capillarity and total and effective porosity are obtained by measuring the amount of distilled water taken up by a sample. Details of these laboratory-based operations are included in Section 2.13 of this chapter. The effect of removing soiling on these properties should be determined whenever possible.

Figure 2.11 Photograph of a sandstone surface prior to cleaning viewed by scanning electron microscopy at approximately 15 mm from the outer surface. (J. Kelly)

Figure 2.12 A Rilem tube in use on a sandstone surface to which a water-repellent coating had been applied. The coating had begun to break down and this phase of testing was to record water absorption rates prior to removal of the coating. The Rilem tubes were also used once on-site trials to remove the coating had been undertaken to establish the effect of the removal processes.

Comparative water absorption rates can be measured on site using a Rilem tube (also known as a Karsten tube). A 150 mm (6 in.) graduated clear tube with a reservoir at one end is fixed to the stone surface by means of a putty gasket and filled with water. The rate at which a fixed amount of water inside is absorbed by the stone is recorded against time, e.g. 10, 30 and 60 minutes to provide information on the water absorption rate primarily by capillary uptake of the masonry. Because of the wide range of variations, even within a single stone, comparative measurements need to be taken in the same position. The results will be comparative and can be considered quantitative only, i.e. uptake as amount per unit area, but can nevertheless be extremely useful as part of the survey and on-site trial phases. Although the tubes have been difficult to obtain in the UK in recent years, they do provide very useful information.

Colour measurement

Portable electronic colour meters are available which will record the hue, lightness and saturation of the colour of a masonry surface at any stage during the cleaning process. Readings need to be made under the same light conditions to be comparable. Cleaning-induced colour changes need to be significant to be regarded as conclusive. Confused results can arise from the inherent colour variations that are present in many stones. Agreement needs to be reached on what is the 'natural' colour of the stone and the extent to which this has been affected by soiling or cleaning procedures as distinct from weathering (patina).

2.11 ANALYSIS AND CHEMICAL CLEANING

Analytical investigations such as those described should be undertaken as part of on-site trials and evaluations, and at later stages as a monitoring process of the effects of the cleaning. The results of chemical cleaning can be evaluated by a well-established range of analytical processes.

Analytical techniques	Before cleaning	Immediately following cleaning	12 months after cleaning
1. Petrographic analysis – assessment of thin sections	●	●	●
2. Physical analysis – determination of capillarity and porosity	●	●	●
3. Chemical analysis (a) Water-soluble content of the sample (soluble salts)	●	●	●
(b) Acid-soluble content of the sample (acid susceptibility)	●		
(c) Solvent-soluble content (pollutants/soiling)	●		●?
4. SEM examination of the surface	●	●	●

2.12 ANALYSIS AND ABRASIVE CLEANING

Abrasive cleaning is an area of masonry cleaning which has largely escaped analytical investigation. Assessments are frequently made on the basis of visual inspections of cleaned and uncleaned surfaces, and by touching in order to attempt to feel any increase in surface roughness.

An adequate assessment should determine what alterations have been made to the stone surface (i.e. surface roughening and surface loss) and the amount of soiling that has been left behind (i.e. the effectiveness of the cleaning). Visual inspection is usually sufficient to determine the effect on arrises, cracks and other exposed defects.

1. Inspection of cleaned surfaces under magnification of ×30 through a field microscope should be applied to all abrasively cleaned test areas. Damage visible under microscopic inspection will cause similar accelerated weathering, as will severe, large-scale damage which is visible to the naked eye. The level of damage which is visible by eye must be considered high.

2. Damage is more readily recognizable in a mould of the surface made in opaque, coloured or silicone rubber as the recesses are presented in relief. Silicone rubber moulds are more precise because of the flexibility of the material and its ability to withdraw from recesses without damage.

3. Touch is a surprisingly effective detector of increased surface roughness, particularly where the edge of the cleaned area is within the confines of a masonry unit.

4. A petrographic thin section of the edge of a trial cleaning zone showing both cleaned and uncleaned surface would be particularly informative as to how much stone has been removed by the cleaning and how much soiling has been left behind. The edge of such a trial area should be neatly defined with a metallic strip for the differences to be contained within the normal width of a thin section slide, and for an accurate comparison of the two surfaces.

5. The use of raking light and photography on test areas before and after cleaning can confirm that surface loss and roughening occurred earlier than visual assessment alone could tell. However, limitations should again be expected because it is not possible to remove just the soiling so that the stone can be viewed in its undamaged state without its covering and infilling of pollutants or other matter.

6. The Form Talysurf method is used on laboratory samples to measure roughness of the surfaces before and after abrasive cleaning trials. It works by tracking a fine diamond-tipped needle over the surface of the sample and recording the profile on a chart. It requires destructive sampling of the building surface, and as the same surface cannot be examined more than once, it is not a widely used analytical procedure.

7. Scanning electron microscopy (SEM) enables examination of the surface at very high magnifications at which dislodgement of grains can be easily seen. As the area inspected is extremely small compared with the size of the masonry unit from which it was removed, it may be necessary to take numerous samples.

8. Determination of weight loss due to abrasive cleaning or removal of masonry and soiling from the building surface undertaken by the weighing of stone samples before and after abrasive cleaning in order to determine weight loss and hence loss of stone surface is usually impractical as destructive sampling is required. The results are unlikely to be of great value unless the soiling and stone removed are separated and weighed.

9. The collection and analysis of dusts and/or rinse waters will confirm whether these contain soiling or masonry particles.

2.13 ANALYTICAL APPROACH TO SANDSTONE, ITS CLEANING, REPAIR AND TREATMENT[5]

The belief that the identification of a stone as 'sandstone' is sufficient basis for understanding its processes of alteration and decay is now recognized as totally inadequate, particularly regarding its cleaning. The term 'sandstone' is a general description for a group of rocks which are detrital, quartz-rich sediments with grain sizes varying from 2.00 to 0.0625 mm. It in no way reflects the wide variation of mineralogical, physical and chemical characteristics found in the stones within this general classification. Lack of recognition of these variations has in the past led to many inappropriate cleaning methods and remedial treatments being applied to sandstone surfaces, causing discolouration and accelerated decay rates.

Many of these problems can be avoided if an analytical approach to sandstone cleaning is adopted. The analytical services of specialist

geologists can provide invaluable additional information to professionals such as architects and can avoid many of the problems which have
unfortunately become familiar. The correct interpretation of on-site
factors, integrated with laboratory analysis, can be translated into
appropriate cleaning and remedial work recommendations. However,
the reality is that specialist geologists with the requisite experience and
understanding of masonry walls, weathering, soiling and deterioration
are rare. Without this understanding, data provided can be hard to
understand, irrelevant, misinterpreted or misleading. It is necessary to
ensure that results will be usable and assist in the decision-making
process.

On-site investigation/assessment

On-site investigation of stonework should be directed towards
obtaining visual identification of the apparent stone types present. This
will, of necessity, be based on colour and such characteristics as may be
observed with the naked eye or hand lens, for example, grain size or
other textural features such as banding or lamination. The occurrence of
any alteration of the stone surfaces due to the action of algae, lichen,
pollutants or efflorescence, together with granulation, scaling or
exfoliating elements, should also be noted.

No local consideration of a particular problem should exclude an
assessment of the condition of the whole facade. Decay and staining
frequently relate to poor building maintenance and remedial work to
joints, flashings, copings and rainwater disposal goods. The effect of
these, as well as the design of the facade, should always be taken into
account.

Sampling

On the completion of preliminary assessment of stone types present and
the range or nature of their alteration, samples should be taken which
reflect these variations and which will be useful in the proposed
programme of analysis. With due consideration for the aesthetic
integrity of the masonry, it is usual that the larger the number of
samples available, the more the results of analysis will be representative
of the materials present. The cost implications of this must be
considered. Even quite small, carefully selected samples, with proper

preparation and analytical techniques, can provide an adequate data-base.

Sampling needs to take into account the history of the structure, as far as sequence of construction and remedial works is concerned. There is usually no guarantee that a large structure which may have been built over a five-year period or more, and maintained by various people since then, will have had one source of stone or that the quality of stone will be constant. Samples should therefore be gained over as wide an area as possible and include the extremities of a facade. Each elevation should be sampled as the orientation of a building can give significant variation in the results due to different weathering and decay regimes. The samples should include all aspects of the current stone condition and be taken from all identifiable stone types. Samples of original and repointing mortars should also be taken.

The location of samples on the structure and their relationship to any failures of structure or detailing should be noted. A description of the sample methods should accompany each sample. Also, each sample should be packed separately and be clearly labelled with all relevant information.

It is preferable that the sampling should be carried out by personnel from the analysing facility who can be expected to be responsible for correct sampling. This should, of course, always follow discussion with the owner or the owner's delegated agent.

Laboratory analysis

Laboratory-based work is necessary to elucidate fully the physical and chemical characteristics of the stones. When the surfaces to be cleaned are of sandstone, this level of investigation should certainly be undertaken. However, not all cleaning jobs can afford the cost of such analysis. In other instances, refusal to undertake analysis results from resistance to change or lack of prior planning for its inclusion. In these instances, reliance on the experience of professionals and operatives increases greatly. It should be remembered that the total cost of analysis depends on the type and number of tests done. Useful information based on select testing, avoiding the most expensive methods, can be obtained economically.

Petrological analysis

Petrological analysis entails the systematic examination of stone sample, both in thin section and hand specimen. The purpose is to identify or classify a stone type. Even where the stone type is identified in historical records, such an investigation is recommended for the purpose of confirmation or to note any variation from an expected norm.

Examination of a hand specimen of stone will usually confirm whether it is representative of stone generally used on the building. The examination of an unprepared sample is carried out visually and using low- to medium-power microscopy. However, it is possible for two stones which appear similar under visual inspection to have significantly different grain or binder materials which would alter decision-making regarding cleaning and replacement stone selection. Petrographic examination of samples would reveal such differences.

A sufficient number of petrological thin sections should be prepared from the hand specimens in order to determine the mineralogical and textural nature of the material.

Inspection of samples by this method will reveal important physical characteristics regarding the internal structure of the stone, including degree of cohesion, the nature of the porosity, grain size, grain shape and grain sorting, all of which contribute to its properties. Importantly, the mineralogy of the cementing materials is identified, including the state of alteration of the minerals which, coupled with the textural and physical characteristics mentioned, are principally responsible for the durability or inherent weakness of a particular stone.

Due to the limits of magnification and resolution inherent in light microscopy, the analysis may need to be supported, where appropriate, by other methods. Those most commonly employed are X-ray diffraction (XRD) and the scanning electron microscope (SEM). Both methods are expensive but are worth using selectively. SEM enables close range examination and photography of stone surfaces. Until recently, the technique could only be used on surfaces which had been coated with gold. New environmental SEM does not require gold coating but it is extremely expensive. With SEM and XRD it is possible to assess closely the effect of cleaning processes. The mineralogy of the individual elements and their textural relationships can be determined.

Physical analysis

While the differences apparent in the various sandstone types will be determined from petrological analysis, it is the physical characteristics which will largely control the ingress and movement of water. The majority of processes which are detrimental to stonework require the presence of water for their operation, and it is the physical characteristics of porosity and capillarity which determine the rate and amount of water uptake.

(a) Capillarity determination

The capillary characteristics are generally calculated from the uptake of deionized or distilled water into a stone sample by surface contact with a wetted, absorbent pad. The amount of water taken up is calculated against the dry weight of sample and recorded against time. From these measurements a capillary curve may be plotted. When such measurements are carried out under similar conditions, a graphic illustration of the capillarity of a sample may be compared to other stone types or to modified samples of same stone. Furthermore, from these results the capillary coefficient of the stone type may be determined. The observations may, of course, be applied to the determination of a drying curve.

Comparative water absorption rates can be measured on site using a Rilem tube (see Section 2.10 earlier it this chapter).

(b) Porosity determination

The uptake of water into a stone will be determined largely by its capillary system. However, the effect of the water within the stone, either alone or together with contained contaminates, will depend on the extent and nature of the pore system.

Two methods may be used to determine porosity:

1. Mercury porosimetry. This method is used to determine the pore size distribution of a stone. Air is removed from the sample and mercury is forced into the voids gradually. The amount of mercury entering the pores and the pressure required to achieve this are indicative of the volume of pores penetrated and the pore sizes.
2. Water uptake at atmospheric pressure and temperature (APT) and uptake under vacuum. Unlike capillary testing, these tests are carried out by controlled immersion and saturation of the sample.

Both methods have their limitations which must be correctly interpreted. With the water method, the pores are either filled completely or not. From the amount of water taken up under both normal atmospheric pressure and vacuum, effective and total porosity may be determined together with water absorption coefficient, saturation coefficient and density. This information is useful in several ways, particularly for assessing the susceptibility of the stone to frost damage.

The use of mercury porosimetry allows the determination of both the total porosity and the relative amounts of pores of known diameter. This allows a calculation of the relative amounts of macro-pores to micro-pores. The division between these is an arbitrary one based on earlier petrological work. The present division at 5 mm diameter is under review. Again, these data are significant as an indicator of the ability of the stone to withstand internal pressure originating from either freezing water or salt hydration. The shortcomings of the mercury porosity method are that certain assumptions must be made concerning the pore geometry of the stone, and that the size of the mercury molecule limits measurements to pores of 32 Ångstroms (0.0032 μm) diameter or greater.

However, both methods have their application in determining the characteristics of the stone and with careful interpretation can provide a valuable insight into the material and its alteration.

Chemical analysis

Chemical analysis involves determination of the water-soluble, acid-soluble and solvent-soluble contents of the stone.

Chemical analysis can be developed to a considerable extent by interpretation of the results of petrological analysis. Unfortunately, contaminants, whether derived from alteration of the original chemistry of the stone or by ingress of extraneous matter, are often extremely fine-grained. They may be dispersed through an area which is large in relation to their amount. In addition, the amount of contaminants present may be small relative to the damage caused by their presence. These factors tend to make their identification by direct observation time-consuming and problematical.

With few exceptions, the stones utilized for building and monumental work do not contain appreciable amounts of water-soluble material, and therefore where such material is present, it may be regarded as a contaminant. Similarly, by the use of other solvents, the chemistry relevant to decay processes may be more closely defined.

(a) Water soluble content

Using deionized water, soluble materials may be extracted for analysis. Total analysis may be carried out, but it is considered sufficient to determine the cations and anions which constitute the main classes of soluble salts known to occur within inorganic building materials. It is essential, however, that such analysis be quantitative with regard to the total water-soluble contaminants and to their relative amounts. The techniques most readily available for this determination are atomic absorption, inductively coupled plasma spectroscopy and ion chromatography.

(b) Acid-soluble content

The acid-soluble content is relevant where the stone type under analysis has been previously noted as having a carbonate content. The determination of the total carbonate content is needed in order to assess the response of the stone to a polluted environment. The loss of a calcareous mineralogy will have a direct effect on the stone, owing to loss of its cementing mineralogy or its conversion to a different mineralogy. In the latter respect the dissolution of the stone in acidic water may also have a detrimental effect on adjacent non-calcareous stonework, similar to that observed at times between limestones and sandstones. Furthermore, sandstones with a clay content may have a greater susceptibility to acidic waters.

(c) Solvent-soluble content

The solvent-soluble content aspects of the chemical analysis is mainly directed to the nature of soiling of pollutants other than those mentioned above. While the presence of unburnt fossil fuels and their residues is thought of largely in terms of surface disfigurement, they can contain materials which catalyse or assist other decay mechanisms. As their presence as the dark components of soiling crusts is often the reason for the initiation of an intervention programme, determination of their nature is an important preliminary to the selection of appropriate cleaning methods. This aspect of analysis is also useful in identifying the presence of previous treatment intended to be water repellent.

2.14 CONCLUSIONS AND THE APPROACH TO CLEANING

With the completion of a sequence of analysis as outlined above, an understanding of the nature of the stone substrate and its alteration will be available, upon which a programme of intervention may be reasonably based. This will allow a choice of methods and materials applicable to the problems of the stonework as determined rather than as assumed.

From the examination of correctly selected thin sections and from the use of chemical profiling, it will be apparent that soiling or alteration are not confined to the surface of the stonework. There are no universal sandstone cleaners, just as there are no universal limestone or granite cleaners. Note must be taken of the nature and the specific condition of the stone substrate so that the cleaning approach can be tailored to suit.

To conclude, it is very important that the testing of any proposed cleaning materials is viewed as an integral part of the programme of analysis and assessment. The success of the process described relies heavily on the quality of the professional interpretation given to the many factors.

REFERENCES

1. Andrew, C. and Crawford, E. (1992) Conservation and planning considerations in stone cleaning, *Stone Cleaning and the Nature, Soiling and Decay Mechanisms of Stone*, Proceedings of the International Conference held in Edinburgh, UK, 14–16 April 1992. London: Donhead, p.195.
2. Crawford, E. (1992) Coming clean, *Context* No.35, (The Association of Conservation Officers), September, p.20.
3. Ashurst, J. and Dimes, F.G. (eds) (1990) *Conservation of Building and Decorative Stone*. London: Butterworth/Heinemann, Volume 2, p.33.
4. Kelly, J., Lithan Ltd, personal communication.
5. The bulk of this section was first published as: Ashurst, N. and Kelly, J. (1990), The analytical approach to stone, its cleaning, repair and treatment, *Conservation of Building and Decorative Stone*. London: Butterworth/Heinemann.

Chapter Three

Soiling

3.1 SOILING AS A CAUSE OF DECAY

The primary purpose of cleaning is to enhance the durability of a surface by removing the soiling. This argument is frequently forgotten in an era when discussion of the aesthetics of building cleaning is paramount but it must not be forgotten.

> Dirt may contain deleterious deposits which would attack the surface; dirt provides a surface condition which may promote chemical reactions involving atmospheric gases; dirty areas remain wet after rain for longer periods than do clean surfaces, so that chemical reaction, freeze–thaw and growth of micro-organisms are promoted; and dust may act as a catalyst for converting atmospheric pollutants to sulphuric and nitric acids which attack stone.[1]

Soiling on masonry surfaces restricts the movement of moisture into and out of its surface to one degree or another. This will depend on the thickness of the soiling and on its nature, that is, to what degree the soiling itself is permeable to water. It is usually found that soiling will have sufficiently different physical properties from the masonry behind to be considered a source of deterioration which needs to be removed.

The reduction by soiling of water uptake through the outer layers relative to the body of a stone is only of possible benefit if water is prevented from entering behind such a surface layer by other routes. But it is not just the physical characteristics of soiling that are of concern.

The removal of encrusted soiling which frequently contains soluble salts and pollutants is important to the on-going well-being of masonry. During wetting and drying phases the salts can be transported into the stone. The encrustations will provide a continuing source of damage if they are not removed.

From the point of view of the stone's health, cleaning must be complete to be effective. Soiling does not exist only as a superficial layer but can be intimately associated with the mineral elements of the original surface and extend inwards from the surface layers. The soiling needs to be removed from the depths of all crevices.

The soiling of building facades which leads to changes in their appearance is a complex phenomenon involving the deposition of several types of pollutant in a complexity of ways. Soiling is frequently subdivided into two main groups: non-biological and biological soiling. Discussion of these follows.

3.2 SOILING AND WEATHERING PATTERNS

The orientation, architectural features and fenestration pattern of a facade will be the main determinants in the run-off pattern of rainwater. They combine to establish zones of protection and zones of water run-off. Architectural protrusions will cause diversions to what would otherwise be a vertical flow path, concentrating run-off into localized streams. In the absence of properly detailed sills, areas of masonry beneath fenestration will be subject to increased volumes of water compared with stonework nearby. Stonework beneath projections will be protected from rainwater run-off. Defective joints in overhangs will concentrate run-off on the stonework beneath. Parapets, pinnacles, cornices, hood moulds, sills and pilasters are typically more heavily saturated than plain ashlar walling. In many instances, soiling on protruding, free-standing and even flat areas of a facade would not be uniform. Many different degrees and tenacities of soiling are the result and the reason that one cleaning method is rarely successful when applied throughout.

The detailed nature of the surface material will be an important factor

Figure 3.1 In the early 1970s, most of London's buildings were as soiled with adherent particulates as this portion of the Palace of Westminster (Houses of Parliament). Since that time, most surfaces have been cleaned several times as they continue to resoil due to the urban pollution. Every building will have a characteristic soiling pattern which will re-emerge as soiling develops. (Department of Ancient Monuments and Historic Buildings)

in affecting its soiling. Two adjacent stones of similar appearance and undergoing the same soiling conditions can develop distinctly different soiling patterns as the result of differences in porosity, pore size distribution, capillary systems, surface tension forces and surface texture, characteristics which affect the movement of moisture into and out of the stone.

Limestones and sandstones generally respond to varying degrees of exposure and water washing in contrasting manners which enable identification of general stone type. The soiling pattern of limestone buildings is for clean limestone in rainwashed areas and dirty stone in sheltered and semi-sheltered zones. Rainwashed surfaces are kept clean by the constant removal of soiling and particles of stone surface. They may be weathered but are generally sound. In contrast, sheltered surfaces of limestone typically comprise encrusted soiling, often with the blistering and splitting of the sulphated stone surface beneath.

The soiling pattern on sandstone buildings is the reverse. The heaviest, blackest appearance on sandstone surfaces is in areas which are most exposed to saturation. Areas which are regularly wetted and dried tend to accumulate dirt. These are also the areas where the inherent patina of the sandstone will be most developed. They are consequently the most difficult areas to clean to uniform colour.

The weathering pattern of a facade can never be lost: it will reappear after cleaning, eventually.

3.3 CONSTITUENTS OF SOILING

The constituents of soiling on external masonry surfaces are usefully categorized as:

> Non-biological.
> Biological.
> Stains.

Non-biological soiling

Non-biological soiling comprises:[2]

1. Airborne particulate matter deposited on the building facade such as soot, vehicle exhausts and industrial chemical emissions.

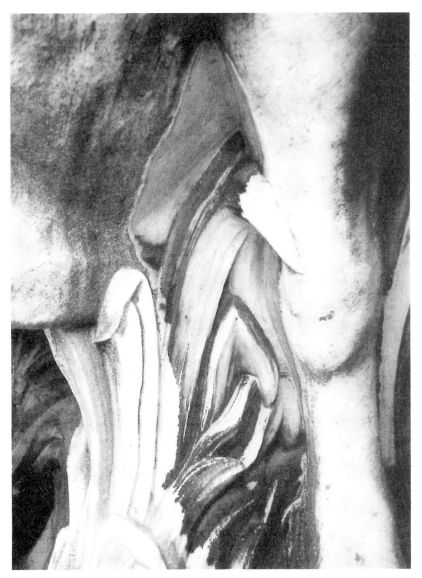

Figure 3.2 Weathering and soiling patterns must be assessed on a small scale if the constituents of soiling are to be adequately understood. Differences between weathered and protected surfaces on this marble sculpture (the America Group at the Albert Memorial) are marked and will require different cleaning approaches. On weathered surfaces, the soiling is principally biological. Within recesses, the predominant constituent is atmospheric.

2. Soluble material from within the masonry drawn to the surface by evaporating moisture. During this process mineralogical changes may take place within stone and staining may result at the stone surface. It should be appreciated that natural waters,

rainfall, for example, are naturally acidic even in the absence of pollution and their dissolving effects are greater than would be expected with pure water.

Non-biological soiling on masonry surfaces is, therefore, a combination of foreign matter which has become attached to the masonry and the product's alteration of the masonry which serves to bind it to the surface. The masonry surface and its soiling are closely integrated. All cleaning of masonry must involve consideration of the effects of the selected cleaning processes, weighing the effect of immediate losses directly caused by the cleaning processes against possible long-term losses and the effect of leaving the dirt on the surface and not cleaning. With limestones which are heavily polluted with crusts, the original stone surface and detail may lie within the crust and will not be the stone surface exposed by total removal of crust.

Airborne particulate matter[3]

(a) Atmospheric constituents and
      pollutants

This comprises airborne particulate matter in the atmosphere. Pollutants may be either naturally occurring particles such as dust, or man-made pollutants such as soot, industrial chemical emissions and vehicle exhaust emissions. As air quality has improved as the result of legislation, the predominance of certain man-made pollutants has given way to others (see below). Modern urban atmospheres can also contain gaseous pollutants which are significant as agents of stone decay.

(b) Aerosols

Air contains many types of aerosols comprising both particulates and gaseous pollutants. The particulate matter of aerosols includes sulphates, nitrates, ammonia, silicates, metal cations, soot, hydrocarbons, etc. The finest constituents of these (less than 0.1μm) include the products of the burning of fossil fuels. Mostly they are deposited by wet deposition processes.

(c) Soot

Soot is particles in a size range $0.1-1\,\mu$m. They are more responsible than coarse particles for the soiling of facades. It is believed that the soiling is mainly the result of dry deposition, with wet deposition of soot being of minor importance.

(d) Particulates and other pollutants

Larger particulates do not remain on building surfaces for long. Sulphates may produce soiling by reacting with constituents within the stone, for example, iron.

Black crusts have four basic components:

1. Inorganic, airborne particulates, for example, soil particles, dust, 'fly ash'.
2. Organic, airborne particulates, for example, plant remains, pollen.
3. Inorganic precipitates, perhaps produced in situ, for example, gypsum.
4. Organic growth in or on the crust, for example, bacteria, fungi and bird excrement.

Number 3 is instrumental in bonding the whole together. Salts are also an important part of the crust.[4]

The deposition of particulate soiling

A building will experience a multitude of micro-climates, each of which will set up particular conditons for the way it receives soiling.

As wind flows around the building, areas of pressure, suction and turbulence are created. Under light wind conditions (i.e. minimum turbulence), particles tend to be deposited on windward faces. In stronger wind conditions, the increased negative pressures and eddies on leeward faces will tend to concentrate dirt in these locations.[5] Temperature has an important role in controlling the amount of pollution present and the way it is deposited. Water is a major vehicle in transporting soiling to a building facade.

Mist in the air causes coagulation of particles and hence their sedimentation. Rain and other forms of atmospheric water can capture particles and atmospheric pollutants and precipitate them. The concentration of pollutants is particularly high in foggy weather so the geographical location and the climate affecting a building will be significant determinants of the way in which, and rate at which, it soils.[6]

The size and shape of particles largely determines the way in which they attach to a building's surface. Particulate dirt which adheres to masonry by a combination of adsorption and electrostatic attraction can usually be removed by simple cleaning methods. However, dirt layers

partially incorporated in a crust of deterioration products, efflorescences, recrystallized carbonate materials and/or leached cementing
materials are more strongly held in place and therefore significantly
resistant to removal by simple methods.[7]

The history of soiling

Buildings in the UK have been exposed to the environment and its
pollution for many centuries. During this time, the nature of pollution
has changed significantly, as has our understanding of masonry soiling
and approaches to preventing or removing it.[8]

The shift from wood to coal as principal fuel began in south-east
England in the thirteenth century. In the late sixteenth century,
following the widespread construction of household chimneys, in
England, and London particularly, coal began to be used domestically.
The success of coal as fuel increased to the extent that by the mid-
eighteenth century, London was using more than one million tons a year
and levels of the traditional pollutants – smoke and sulphur dioxide –
rose dramatically. Concentrations of these peaked at the turn of the
century. John Evelyn's view on the physical and visual effect of pollution
on architecture is recorded in his book on air pollution *Fumifugium*
(1661) which he wrote because smoke from the chimneys near Scotland
Yard prevented him from viewing the palace of Charles II, Whitehall.[9]
The soiling and damaging effect of coal-fired pollution on London stone
was recognized from the seventeenth century on. The nineteenth
century responses to it included the use of more durable and more
washable materials such as glazed tiles, bricks, marble and glass, for
example the terracotta of the Victoria and Albert Museum.

Westminster Abbey, the Houses of Parliament, Hampton Court
Palace and Westminster Hall were the subject of an alternative approach
to the problem: the application of surface treatments, or indurations as
they were then called.[10] The solutions were supposed to prevent, or at
least reduce, further decay and to prevent surfaces from taking up soiling
from the atmosphere. Solutions applied included linseed oil, beeswax,
paraffin, gums, resins, silicate solutions of various types. None of these
were effective in halting subsequent stone decay and frequently within
very short periods after application, their detrimental effects were
noted.[11] Many produced unacceptable colour changes and induced
accelerated pitting and spalling of stone surfaces. The failure of
indurations as a method of solving the problems of stone deterioration
and soiling led to a return to stone replacement. This century, the most

significant change has been the widespread adoption of washing and other methods of cleaning as a principal technique in the treatment and preservation of masonry.

> The environmental situation in the UK deteriorated through the nineteenth century and the first half of the twentieth as the consumption of coal for domestic heating and power generation increased. Following the introduction of clean air legislation (1956) and the availability of alternative methods for domestic heating the situation has changed.[12]

The role of diesel fumes

Analysis of fuel type used in the UK showed that between 1979 and 1989, there was a substantial reduction in emissions from coal combustion but an almost doubling of emissions from diesel.[13] This means that while the contribution of coal burning to pollution has declined, emissions from diesel vehicles have become a major source of soiling in urban areas. The diesel fumes from engines in buses, lorries and taxis are now recognized as the main cause of resoiling of city buildings. Diesel exhaust is a rich source of very fine carbon

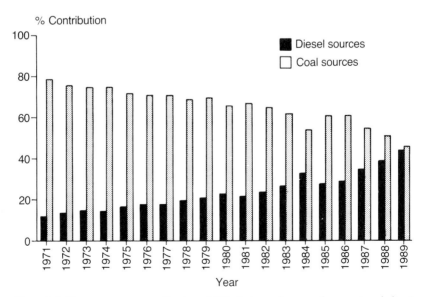

Figure 3.3 The percentage contribution of UK dark smoke mass from coal and diesel combustion from 1971 to 1989. (From Mansfield, T.A. (1992), p.86, table supplied by Ron Hamilton.)

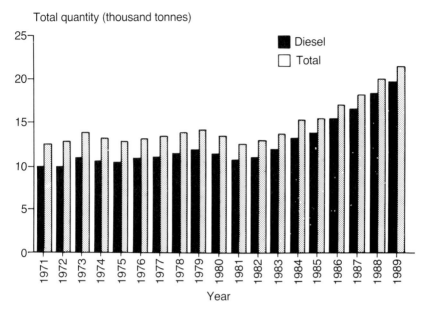

Figure 3.4 Diesel and total PEC emissions (in thousand tonnes) for the UK from 1971 to 1989. (From Mansfield, T.A. (1992), p.87, table supplied by Ron Hamilton.)

particles known as particulate elemental carbon (PEC). These originate from the incomplete combustion of carbon-based fuels. Their character-istics and effects are described by Trudie Mansfield as follows:

> Although PEC is chemically inert, particles produced by diesel engines are very small, being about 0.02μm in size and they are very sticky in nature because of their hydrocarbon content. Thus, a diesel particle landing on a surface is more likely to become strongly adhered to it. It is additionally much less water soluble than a suspended soil particle which may be readily removed by rain washing. PEC's surface tension properties have implications for potentially damaging reactions which may occur within the patina of a building's facade. Acidic gases such as sulphur and nitrogen oxides can in turn become easily absorbed onto the surface of such particles and once deposited on a soiled stone surface may act synergystically with it. Also, PEC, due to its electronic structure and π-electron system, may aid in the catalytic con-version of such acidic gases to the sulphate and nitrate forms respectively.
>
> Once sulphuric and nitric acid are present on the building fabric surface, they may then react, for example, with limestone and convert it into gypsum or calcium nitrate respectively. These latter

compounds are more soluble and leachable with rainfall than limestone and thus elevated erosion rates may occur. Calcium nitrate is more leachable than gypsum and considering the emissions of nitrogen oxides are increasing within the ambient atmosphere (over 50 per cent of the national emission of nitrogen oxides are vehicularly derived), this may be a factor in explaining the fact that rates of building erosion are similar to when ambient levels of pollution of smoke and sulphur dioxide were much greater than they are now.

. . . Although the impact of such carbon-catalysed reactions has not been well studied, it may well be that soiling may not only be a nuisance in terms of aesthetic blight, but also in terms of enhancing the rate of fabric erosion. [14]

In 1991, the European Community is addressing the problem of emissions from new diesel-engined trucks, buses and passenger cars and has received recommendations that the same be done for existing diesel-engined trucks. Nevertheless, it is anticipated that diesel's contribution to the resoiling of UK buildings will be dominant for some time to come, especially as diesel cars now represent 50 per cent of new car sales.

Redeposition of particulate soiling on cleaned buildings

A previous study undertaken by Trudie Mansfield at the Urban Pollution Research Centre of Middlesex Polytechnic aimed to investigate the nature of diesel particulates and also determined soiling potentials for a variety of materials at a range of London sites. It was discovered that the resoiling of surfaces, and hence buildings, was fast. [15] A model for the soiling of building surfaces developed by Newby, Mansfield and Hamilton showed that light reflectance of a surface at an urban site can fall to 60 per cent of its initial value after five years. [16]

Subsequent studies set up to measure soiling rates within the urban environment have generally established that soiling appears to be very rapid during the first period of exposure (a decrease of 32 per cent of the original reflectance within seven days). [17] Resuspended road dust and soil-derived particles may be deposited on materials but are more likely to be removed by rainfall than a deposited diesel particle.

Portland stone buildings in urban environments may need to be recleaned approximately every five to ten years. In town or rural environments this period could extend to ten to fifteen years or more. The pattern of resoiling which has been observed in cities throughout the UK indicates a predominance of new soiling at ground to third floor levels, with darker soiling at ground level where diesel fumes are most concentrated, grading to lighter at higher levels. Where rain washing is restricted to these lower levels by surrounding buildings, the role of diesel particles in resoiling lower levels of masonry is less conclusive.

Biological soiling

Biological soiling, the second category of soiling found on masonry surfaces, comprises small-scale surface and subsurface growths and larger-scale plant life. It comprises principally algae, fungi, lichens and bacteria growing on and within the masonry surface. Some of these organisms, and higher plants, can also cause serious damage to masonry units and masonry structures.

All forms of biological soiling have specific requirements for water,

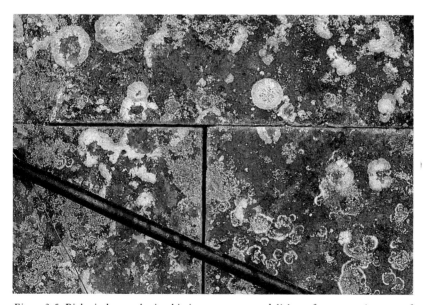

Figure 3.5 Biological growth, in this instance moss and lichen, forms a major part of masonry soiling on limestone surfaces in rural environments, to the extent that it represents much of the historical patina of many historic buildings and structures. It is easy to understand the reluctance of many owners to have it removed. The effect of biological growth on the masonry beneath must be understood so that its contribution to the deterioration of the substrate can be determined. Not all biological growths on masonry are benign.

light, temperature, pH and nutrition. The alteration of any of these beyond its range of preferred conditions may kill off the growth of a particular organism.

Many micro-organisms show a remarkable ability to adapt to temperature and moisture cycles. Photosynthetic organisms need light and carbon dioxide to develop. However, some micro-organisms can exist over a wide range of pH levels; for example, some bacteria will grow happily between the pH values of 6 and 9 and numerous fungi will tolerate pH values from 2 to 11.[18]

Biological soiling may affect masonry differently from atmospheric soiling but it does not always look different. Certain cyano bacteria and fungi soiling appear identical to atmospheric soiling until viewed under a microscope. Run-off from copper will kill these growths.[19] The case for the removal of biological soiling needs to be assessed on both technical and aesthetic grounds.

Bacteria

Bacteria are a group of very small organisms which are often recognized by the chemical and biological changes they bring about.[20] However, heavy deposits can exist in immense concentrations with algae and fungi.[21] Certain bacterial organisms assimilate nitrogen from the atmosphere to form ammonia and other nitrogenous compounds whilst others oxidize ammonia to form nitrous and nitric acids. All these products attack limestone, marble and other calcareous substrates which provide a habitat suited to their growth. According to Palmer, 'micro-organisms can be responsible for the complete spectrum of building stone deterioration: from relatively benign aesthetic damage to severe disintegration of the substrate resulting in collapse of the structure.'[22] Compared with other deterioration mechanisms, the role may be a minor one but it may establish conditions for accelerated weathering of other kinds.

To date, no satisfactory technique exists by which micro-biological activity can be quantified directly in stone environments. The break-down mechanisms are complex. Some of them involve colour changes to the stone which need to be understood as part of a pre-cleaning study.

The effects of various cleaning processes on the communities also need to be understood. It should not be assumed that cleaning of masonry, even by chemical processes, will kill off micro-biological growth. In fact, cleaning may create surfaces with improved growth conditions for some species. According to Palmer, water repellent treatments which can drastically alter the moisture regime of a stone at depth must be understood as it is possible that micro-organisms will grow even better in the presence of such a treatment than without it. [23]

While understanding the microflora of stone may seem peripheral to a cleaning project today, it should be expected that this understanding will be seen as necessary in the coming years.

Since 1986, about twenty-five buildings in Germany have been analysed for contamination by nitrifying bacteria. Two groups of specialized bacteria were found to be involved in, first, oxidizing ammonia to nitrite, and second, oxidizing nitrite to nitrate. Both chemical steps produce salts and/or mineral acids which can cause stone damage. Calcareous sandstones are particularly vulnerable to this sort of attack. The bacteria live in micro-colonies within the stone, surrounded by a film which protects them from dryness and/or toxic agents. Analysis of the German stones found them present at depths of up to 300 mm. [24]

Algae

Algae are usually green when the masonry is wet and black when the surface dries out. Other species of algae which are red, brown and blue in colour are also found. They will be slimy if the surface is moist and in the form of filaments or powders if it is dry.

Algae prefer substrates which are damp and will frequently develop on a wide range of substrates experiencing excessive water run-off, for example a leaking downpipe, or high levels of water retention, for example cornices with inadequate fall or surfaces which have been heavily roughened by an abrasive cleaning process. Algae become darker in appearance as they entrap more and more soot particles. They also darken and begin to die as increasing levels of surface pollution alter the pH of their environment to an unacceptable level. Algal growths which die due to lack of moisture turn black and often remain slightly attached. The dead growth can easily be removed by low pressure rinsing prior to the general cleaning works.

While algae in the main do not rely on the masonry substrate for food, the organic acids they secrete can dissolve the calcium carbonate of limestone, concrete and mortar. Algae can also act on the substrate by inserting cells into the masonry pores. The swelling and shrinking of the cells in response to moisture can have a mechanical influence on the stone and lead to micro-cracking. [25] Algae can serve to retain water on the surface of porous materials and can thereby bring a rise in the moisture content of the underlying substrate. The mossy sheaths of algae when dead can serve as basic nutrition for bacteria or fungi.

Lichens

Lichens are a symbiotic intergrowth of algae and fungi. The algal cells produce the food by photosynthesis while the hyphae of the fungi search for water. Much of the body of the lichen is under the stone or mortar surface but their grey, green, yellow and orange fruiting bodies are seen on the surface.[26] Endolithic lichens live beneath the stone surface entirely. Lichens, more than algae, are substrate-specific, some preferring calcareous surfaces and others siliceous surfaces.

Lichens secrete carbon dioxide and acidic products which can react with calcareous substrates such as limestone, marble, lime render and calcareous sandstone. Certain lichens are attached by a network of fine roots which penetrate several millimetres into masonry, not only through cracks and existing pores but also by attacking the material.[27] The damage to limestone and lime-render surfaces by some species of lichen can be seen readily as etched depressions beneath individual cushions of lichen. Closer range inspection is necessary to confirm the damage caused by other lichen types.

Even if certain lichens are not chemically or mechanically damaging to stone surfaces, their ability to hold moisture in contact with the surface makes their presence undesirable. Even the more durable stone types can be subject to breakdown by lichen.

Lichens do not like the noxious contents of urban environments and are more frequently found in rural areas. Lichens are often a predominant part of the character of historic buildings and frequently considered an important indicator of the ageing process. The effect on the masonry of doing so must be properly evaluated as their attractive appearance can hide their role as contributors to decay.

On relatively smooth and sound surfaces, the removal of lichen usually requires low pressure washing and/or scraping or brushing with hand-held implements, undertaken prior to cleaning work. More sensitive, painstaking methods are required on other surface types and conditions.

Fungi

Fungi can be grey, green, black or brown in colour and often take the form of furry spots or patches on the surface of the substrate.[28] They do not require light in order to grow. Also, as they do not manufacture their own food, organic food must be present on masonry surfaces. Fungi can be found growing in thick deposits of leaf litter and bird droppings or on the dead remains of other organisms.

Fungi have the potential to produce oxalic and citric acids and may therefore contribute to the decay of limestones. Fungal hyphae have been found by several analytical and research bodies throughout the world penetrating into limestone and marble surfaces to considerable depths, travelling along intergranular boundaries.[29]

Plant life to be removed

The cleaning of historical masonry usually involves identification of the forms of plant life present and selection of appropriate techniques and materials for their removal.[30] Plants and other living organisms can provide valuable information as to the condition of a masonry facade by indicating problems such as areas of saturated masonry and zones of defective pointing. Small flowering plants and ferns indicate that sufficient dirt is present for their roots to grow in. They are frequently found growing from heavily weathered joints which need to be cut out, deep tamped and repointed. Some ferns will grow in relatively dry conditions while others require damp. Moss can be found growing in defective or heavily weathered joints which retain moisture.

Ivy (*Hedera helix*) and other creepers can damage historic masonry by the secretions of suckers and tendrils and, more usually, by the mechanical displacements and stresses caused by their growing root and stem structures. Thin shoots which enter the masonry gradually develop into thick stems, forcing masonry units apart. In their quest for moisture, their roots can penetrate deeply into a masonry structure, eventually rendering it unstable. Ivy and trees operate in this manner. Virginia creepers and other related species hold on to masonry surfaces by a multitude of small surface suckers and are generally not considered to be harmful. Their leaf cover can inhibit the drying of masonry.

Treating biological growth[31]

A long-term inhibiting effect on biological growth on some walls may be obtained by the installation of narrow flashing strips of thin-gauge copper. These are tucked into the length of horizontal joints in the masonry at approximately one metre intervals. The effect of rain washing over the strips is to subject the face of the masonry to a mildly toxic wash. A certain amount of light green stain must be anticipated which makes this system unsuitable for very light coloured stones, and of course it will not be effective where detailing on the building tends to throw off the rain.

The treatment for masonry covered with algae, lichen, mosses and small plants often involves the application of a biocide, as described below. The handling and mixing of biocides requires a full COSHH assessment (Control of Substances Hazardous to Health Regulations, 1988 – see Section 8.7, Volume 2) and extensive use of personal protective equipment. Spraying should not be undertaken in the immediate vicinity of other unprotected people or animals. Biocides used must be approved under the Control of Pesticides Regulations, 1986, for use as directed and have a Health and Safety Executive (HSE) approval number.

The general application procedure is:

1. Remove as much plant growth as possible with small spatulas and stiff bristle or non-ferrous soft wire brushes. If the surface below the growth is delicate or liable to be marked or scoured in any way, this preparation must be limited to lifting of cushions of moss.

2. Prepare the solution of biocide to the manufacturer's specification.

3. Fill a pneumatic garden-type sprayer two-thirds full with the diluted biocide. Adjust the nozzle to a coarse spray setting. There should be sufficient pressure at the wand nozzle, after pumping the container, to saturate the surface of the masonry without causing excessive splashing or spray drift.

4. Apply a flood coat. Commence at the top of the vertical surface to be treated and move across horizontally and slowly to allow approximately 100 mm run-down. The next horizontal pass should be made across the previous run-down.

5. Leave the treated area for at least one week. Brush off as much dead growth as possible with bristle brushes, making sure that any adjacent gutters and hoppers are kept clear.

6. Prepare another solution of the acceptable proprietary biocide to the manufacturer's specification.

7. Fill a second pneumatic sprayer with the diluted biocide and apply in the same manner as (4) above.

8. Allow the surface to absorb the solution and carry out a second application.

Provided that the applications are made carefully, there should be little risk to grass or flowers below the treated area. However, as there is always a risk of spillage, it is sensible to lay a sheet over plants on the ground whilst working. In close proximity to ponds containing fish and other aquatic wild life, it would be prudent to carry out mechanical cleaning only to avoid the possibility of contamination during treatment and subsequently due to leaching of biocide from treated surfaces.

Removal of ivy

A length of the main stem of the ivy should be cut out at a convenient

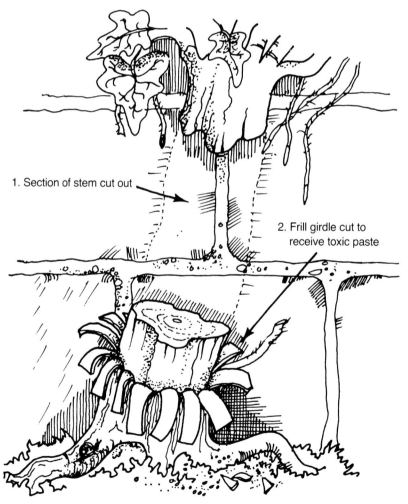

Figure 3.6 Treatment for removal of major ivy growth. (From Ashurst, J. and N. (1988), Volume 1, p.24.) (English Heritage)

height above ground level. The plant may be left in this state to die of its own accord, but it is quite possible for a well-established plant to survive on the wall for up to two years after such an operation. Spraying the plant with an appropriate systemic poison will hasten its destruction. Manufacturer's instructions must be carefully followed.

The parent stem, after cutting, should be cut to a frill girdle and the exposed surfaces coated with a paste made from ammonium sulphamate crystals. Sheet plastic covering should be firmly secured over the treated area. In this condition the root system may be left to absorb the paste and die. The ammonium sulphamate must not be used on masonry surfaces where, in association with lime, it would become a nitrogenous fertilizer. Once again, it is important to adhere to the manufacturer's recommendations on safety and environmental protection.

The removal of the dead plant from the wall may be straightforward, but the temptation to pull off a well-established mat of vegetation with a rope must be resisted. Mature growth must be carefully cut or pulled out of every joint, and wedging of the blocks or deep tamping carried out as work proceeds. Tamping, grouting and pointing, and resetting of stones, especially on wall tops, must all be anticipated as remedial work. Large sections of dead wood must not be left within the core: as they decay, they will remove support and create voids and weaknesses in the wall.

Stains

Water staining on sandstone

Extended periods of water saturation on sandstone surfaces can produce staining to a considerable depth. The staining represents mineralogical colour changes within the stone, and it is usually not possible to remove such soiling without removing excessive amounts of the masonry itself. The temptation to abrade areas of masonry with zones of this type of soiling which are visually unacceptable must be avoided. In many instances, the depth of stone affected by the residual staining will mean that even surface removal by abrasive cleaning will not remove enough of the stain.[32] These marks should be considered deep and permanent.

Post-cleaning staining of limestone

Post-cleaning staining of white coloured Portland stone surfaces is frequently attributed to the dissolution of the surface or subsurface soiling, its migration into the stone in liquid form and its redeposition on the stone surface during the drying out period during cleaning. The staining is not always superficial or water soluble, and its removal can be difficult to achieve.

Iron is a minor constituent in many light-coloured stones, including Portland limestone and white marbles. The term 'latent iron content' is used to describe its presence which only becomes visible at certain times. Some marbles cleaned incorrectly with alkaline cleaning materials may have their latent iron content activated by a chemical cleaning agent and turn brown as a result. This can arise due to the heavy-handed use of alkaline cleaners and their insufficient neutralization. Over saturation with water is often associated with development of this type of staining.

The effect of fire

The colour of stone can be affected by fire. This is particularly noticeable on light-coloured stones. The resultant pink colour is due to oxidation of iron in the stone. The depth of the oxidation is considerable, and as the marks have no negative effect on the stone, there is little point in attempting their removal. There is also the problem of fractures induced by the heat in the surface layers of the stone.

Black soiling deposited on masonry surfaces as the result of fire does not damage the stone. Most of it will be superficial, although there may be a degree of penetration. The soiling will comprise the products of decomposition of wood, fabrics (natural and synthetic) and plastics. It will usually have a significant greasy component and require non-ionic soaps, solvents or mild alkaline cleaners (neutralized) for its removal.

Prior to the cleaning of fire-affected surfaces, the masonry should be inspected to determine whether any surfaces are shattered as the result of thermal shock. Any necessary structural support should, of course, be in place.

Metal stains

Copper stains are usually dilute solutions of copper sulphate or copper chloride which have run off from a cuprous surface above (copper, brass or bronze). 'On contact with limestone or mortar, this alters to a less soluble, blue-green basic copper salt, which remains on the mortar or stone as a stain'.[33] Sandstones are also stained by copper run-off.

Rust stains are deposited on masonry due to run-off from rusting iron or steel. These stains can be dark and intense on masonry surfaces.

Both types of metallic stain are difficult and sometimes impossible to

Figure 3.7 Lack of maintenance and protection of metal features has meant the limestone plinth of this church monument has been stained by rust from the corroding figure of Christ above and by cuprous runoff from the commemorative plaques. The staining has been developing for many years and is deep-seated as a result.

remove, particularly if they have been on the masonry surface for a long time. The depth of masonry affected can be considerable, making only lightening of the stains possible.

Bird droppings

Droppings and nesting materials of pigeons and starlings gradually release acids into masonry surfaces. They must, therefore, be considered sources of deterioration for limestones and calcareous sandstones in particular. The materials also lead to the deposition of soluble salts which will break down any type of stone. At times, the residual marking of starling droppings is difficult to remove completely.

REFERENCES

1. Spry, A.H. (1982) *Principles of Cleaning Masonry Buildings*, Technical Bulletin 3.1. Melbourne: Australian Council of National Trusts, and National Trust of Australia (Victoria), p.4.
2. Robert Gordon Institute of Technology (Masonry Conservation Research Group) (1992) *Stone Cleaning in Scotland: Research Commission Investigating the Effects of Cleaning Sandstone*, Research Report 1, pp.15–23.
3. Ibid., p.16.
4. Whalley, B., Smith, B. and Magee, R. (1992) Effects of particulate air pollutants on materials: investigation of surface crust formation, *Stone Cleaning and the Nature Soiling and Decay Mechanisms of Stone*, Proceedings of the International Conference held in Edinburgh, UK, 14–16 April 1992. London: Donhead, p.230.
5. Verhoef, L.G.W. (ed.) (1988) *Soiling and Cleaning of Building Facades*, Report of Technical Committee 62 SCF RILEM. London: Chapman & Hall, p.17.
6. Robert Gordon Institute of Technology (Masonry Conservation Research Group), (1992) op. cit., p.17.
7. Weiss, N.R. (1985) *Exterior Cleaning of Historic Masonry Buildings (Draft)*. Washington: National Park Service, United States Department of the Interior, p.2.
8. Brimblecombe, P. (1992) A brief history of grime: accumulation and removal of soot deposits on buildings since the 17th century, *Stone Cleaning and the Nature, Soiling and Decay Mechanisms of Stone*, Proceedings of the International Conference held in Edinburgh, UK, 14–16 April 1992. London: Donhead, pp.53–62.
9. Ibid., p.56.
10. Ibid., p.58.
11. Ibid., p.60.
12. Newby, P.T., Mansfield, T.A. and Hamilton, R.S. (1991) Sources and economic implications of building soiling in urban areas, *The Science of the Total Environment*, no.100. Amsterdam: Elsevier, p.350.
13. Mansfield, T.A. (1992) Sources of building soiling and a review of the stone cleaning industry (1991), *Stone Cleaning and the Nature, Soiling and Decay Mechanisms of Stone*, Proceedings of the International Conference held in Edinburgh, UK, 14–16 April 1992. London: Donhead, p.85.
14. Ibid., pp.86–88.
15. Ibid., p.88.
16. Newby, P.T., Mansfield, T.A. and Hamilton, R.S. (1991) op. cit., p.347.
17. Mansfield, T.A. (1992) op. cit.
18. Pochon, J. and De Barjac, H. (1958) Traite de micro-biologie des sols, *Dunod*, p.685 (Reference B) as quoted in: Verhoef, L.G.W. (ed.) (1988) *Soiling and Cleaning of Building Facades*, Report of Technical Committee 62 SCF RILEM. London: Chapman & Hall.
19. Weaver, M.E., personal communication.
20. Ibid.

21. Honeyborne, D.B. (1990) Weathering and decay of masonry, *Conservation of Building and Decorative Stone*. London: Butterworth/Heinemann, Volume 1, p.168.
22. Palmer, R. (1992) Microbiological damage to building stone: analysis and intervention, *Stone Cleaning and the Nature, Soiling and Decay Mechanisms of Stone*, Proceedings of the International Conference held in Edinburgh, UK, 14–16 April 1992. London: Donhead, p.240.
23. Ibid., p.238.
24. Wilimzig, M., Sand, W. and Bock, E. (1992) The impact of stone cleaning on micro-organisms and microbially influenced corrosion, *Stone Cleaning and the Nature, Soiling and Decay Mechanisms of Stone*, Proceedings of the International Conference held in Edinburgh, UK, 14–16 April 1992. London: Donhead, pp.235–236.
25. Verhoef, L.G.W. (1988) op. cit., p.118.
26. Building Research Station (1982) *Control of Lichens, Moulds and Similar Growths*, Digest 139. Garston: HMSO.
27. Verhoef, L.G.W. (1988) op. cit., p.118.
28. Honeyborne, D.B. (1990) op. cit., p.168.
29. Building Research Station (1982), op. cit.
30. Honeyborne, D.B., (1990) op. cit., pp.167–168.
31. The material in this section has been extracted from: Ashurst, J. and N. (1988), *Practical Building Conservation: English Heritage Technical Handbook*. Aldershot: Gower Technical Press, Volume 1, pp. 20–26.
32. Honeyborne, D.B. (1990) op. cit., p.163.
33. Ibid., p.163.

Chapter Four

Masonry Substrates

This chapter considers the constituents and characteristics of sand-stones, limestones, marble, granite, brick and terracotta, the most common masonry materials from which soiling is removed in the UK. Understanding the properties of these materials and the differences between them is the key to their successful cleaning.

Masonry in an external environment experiences changes. Some are natural (weathering and soiling), others are due to man's activities, either directly (damaging remedial works, application of paint) or indirectly (pollution). The nature of soiling and the substances involved differ widely in character and in the degree of difficulty of their removal.

> Urban grime . . . consists of various mixtures of the products of industrial and natural particulate fallout (soot, silica dust, clay, fibres), deposits from aerosols, products formed by reaction between masonry and pollutants (gypsum and other sulphates), hydrocarbons and tarry compounds from car exhausts, . . . micro- and macro-organisms and others. Grime differs from place to place depending on local conditions. Variations include loose dust or mud; thin dark grey to black, shiny and greasy films; thin, hard, tough, dark grey to black, sooty layers; and thick, soft to hard, black crusts.[1]

The nature of soiling and staining is described in Chapter 3 (this volume) in greater depth.

> Historic building materials differ in their tendency to hold grime and in their susceptibility to damage during cleaning because of their wide variation in physical properties (porosity, permeability, hardness, strength, water absorption, texture and structure), in chemical composition, in surface finish (coarsely or finely dressed, polished, smooth, rough), architectural form (smoothed, detailed, carved), and orientation (vertical, sloping or horizontal).[2]

The all-important characteristics of masonry are considered in this chapter.

Deterioration, weathering and soiling

The deterioration, weathering and soiling of masonry are closely inter-related. When considering cleaning, then weathering and deterioration must also be assessed.

Masonry which is exposed to the weather changes as it interacts with its environment. Its colour will change, some of its physical and chemical properties will change, and portions of it will detach at the advanced stages of weathering. A building which is inspected with a view to its cleaning will present much evidence of these interactions. It is essential that the reasons for the deterioration, weathering and soiling of masonry are understood before remedial work, including cleaning, is undertaken.

Visible damage to a masonry surface usually represents the maturing of a particular deterioration process. The powdering of masonry surfaces – the characteristic of the deterioration of certain types of masonry as the result of soluble salt crystallization – is an indication that processes due to weathering or lack of maintenance have been under way for some time, creating the reservoir of soluble salts which are now causing the damage. Soluble salt accumulation does not affect every type of stone in this way. Some remain unaffected. Powdering as granulation may also be due to loss of binder or cement of a stone. The atmosphere in industrialized environments contains acidic, sulphur-based gases and particulate matter of carbon and tar. Vehicles and industries produce pollutants including nitrogen compounds. In industrialized environments, these pollutants gradually take their toll causing the soiling and decay of brickwork and stonework.[3]

The relationship between the surfaces of masonry units which have been modified by their interaction with the environment and its pollutants and the soiling which is adherent to those surfaces is an intimate one. Soiling fills the voids and crevices between the grains or particles of a masonry surface. The removal of soiling without affecting its masonry substrate is very difficult. Consideration of cleaning masonry surfaces cannot be isolated from consideration of the weathering and deterioration of the surfaces to which the soiling is affixed.

4.1 SANDSTONES[4]

Characteristics

Sandstones are naturally formed, sedimentary rocks. In very simple terms, most sandstone types comprise grains of quartz cemented together by matrices of different compositions. All these cementing materials were carried into the original loose, incoherent sand by circulating waters or by wind. A sandstone is produced by deposition of material from solution to bind the sand grains together or by compaction.[5] The most common mineral grains are quartz, micas, feldspars and clays. The cementing medium holds the grain together but does not necessarily completely fill the voids between the grains. Porosity will be found both between and within grains. The effects of the weathering and decay mechanisms on the stone are determined largely by the composition of the cementing medium and physical characteristics such as the nature and extent of the porosity. Sandstones are basically categorized on the basis of the constituents of the cementing medium and grain size.

The most common categories of sandstones are as follows:

Category of sandstone	Cementing medium	Resistance to weathering and acids
Siliceous	Silica (quartz)	Good
Ferruginous	Iron oxides	Good
	Iron hydrates	Acid-sensitive
Calcareous	Calcite	Poor, very acid-sensitive
Dolomitic	Dolomite	Moderate, acid-sensitive
Argillaceous	Clays	Very poor, acid-sensitive

The quartz grains of *siliceous sandstones* are cemented together by silica and are generally very resistant to direct attack by sulphur-based pollutants. They can, however, become very dirty. Iron compounds within these stones can be altered by sulphur-based acids in the air and eventually be deposited on the stone surface in a rusty coloured layer.

Many sandstones are cemented by one or more of the iron compounds, normally the red iron oxides or the brown iron hydrates, or both. They are known as *ferruginous sandstones*. Usually these are light red to deep brown in colour. The colour is caused by the nature and amount of iron cement present. When iron minerals are present in substantial amount, the sandstone may be called carstone.[6]

Calcareous sandstones are sandstones whose cementing component is calcite (calcium carbonate). Calcite is susceptible to attack from airborne acids and calcareous sandstones are therefore prone to deterioration in urban and industrial environments. Calcareous sandstones are also readily attacked by acids which originate from chemical cleaning agents.

Dolomitic sandstones are those whose grains are cemented with dolomite. These tend to be more resistant to acid-based weathering, compared with calcareous sandstones.

Argillaceous sandstones contain significant amounts of clay in their binding media. Because of the particular sensitivity of some clay minerals to the presence of moisture, argillaceous sandstones can break down in the presence of moisture in both polluted and non-polluted environments. They are generally of very poor durability.

Other mineral grains, as distinct from the mineral cementing medium, are present in greater or lesser amounts. Feldspar, commonly in a partially chemically decomposed state and derived from a disintegrated granite, may be present in considerable amounts. If it makes up a third or more of the rock the name *arkose* is used. Grains of the mineral glauconite present as small, rounded, green-coloured aggregates give the rock, particularly when wet, a green cast. The rock is termed a greensand when glauconite is present in any quantity. Other minerals such as gypsum and barytes may rarely be the cementing medium but may locally be present in noticeable amounts.[7]

The term *gritstone* usually refers to stones with angular quartz grains. It is often used for a rock of any composition with grain size between 0.5 and 1.0 mm. The mica flakes in a *micaceous sandstone* are commonly concentrated along bedding planes with their long axes aligned parallel to the bedding. The rock is fissile and will readily split along these planes. If the bedding planes are closely spaced, splitting produces a *flagstone*.

Flint is found as nodules, layers of nodules and more rarely as bands in the top part of the middle and throughout the upper division of the chalk formation. It is compact cryptocrystalline silica.[8]

Weathering

Each sandstone type is a different combination of the minerals listed above. Some of the minerals may be adversely affected by certain stone cleaning techniques while others are easily altered by weathering processes. Analytical investigations are essential to determine the constituents and physical properties of the stone in question to determine how these have already been affected by weathering and to assess whether any characteristics will be adversely affected by the cleaning methods proposed.

All sandstones are susceptible to salt crystallization damage. The built environment includes numerous examples of the breakdown of sandstone surfaces affected by calcium sulphate laden water from limestone surfaces above.

Deterioration of sandstones frequently includes contour scaling. A layer of stone which follows the outer form of the block breaks away with little or no apparent regard to the natural bedding plane of the stone. The phenomenon is the result of the combined effect of air pollution, wetting and drying cycles and heating and cooling cycles on the stone and gypsum and other salts formed within it.

The generally porous structure of sandstones enables water which enters through the face or joints of a block to move with ease. Atmospheric temperature and vapour pressure will determine whether the direction of water movement is inward or outward. If the water dissolves minerals from within the stone, it will deposit these at the stone surface when it evaporates. This can gradually lead to the formation of surface crusts or a relatively impermeable surface layer, often called the patina of a stone, depending on the nature of the salts present, rate of drying, etc. Iron and manganese minerals leached from within a stone by this process are darkly coloured and their deposition on a stone surface can cause staining. This may also take place if the minerals are mobilized by chemical cleaning agents. If the minerals are mobilized to the extent that they can be rinsed from the stone surface when the chemical cleaning agent is removed, 'bleaching' of a stone will

Figure 4.1 The properties of individual stones will be an important determinant of the soiled appearance of a sandstone facade. It is not unusual to find different degrees of soiling between adjacent stones subject to similar weathering conditions. Several of the blocks beneath the sill are exhibiting the final stages of surface or contour scaling.

take place. Some of these minerals may be removed from the outer layer of the stone by natural weathering processes.

The weathering and deterioration of calcareous sandstones is described by Honeyborne as follows:

> Where the stone is heavily rain-washed, the surface will steadily powder away. When the stone is not heavily rain-washed, the acids attack some of the calcite, converting it to more soluble gypsum.

Figure 4.2 Moisture moves into and out of sandstone surface with relative ease. In this case, moisture movement had been inhibited by the application of linseed oil in a misguided attempt to control its rate of natural decay. Cleaning of the surfaces had to include removal of remains of the oily layer.

Some of the gypsum is drawn towards the surface in solution and redeposited as the moisture dries out again. This produces a weakened layer roughly 4 mm below the surface of the stone which blocks the pores of the surface layer. As the temperature varies, the unrestrained gypsum expands or contracts about 1.7 times as much as sandstone. Changes of temperature will therefore create stresses that tend to break the gypsum-rich layer from the underlying sandstone. In time, these layers will peel off.[9]

Prior to peeling, the stone may contain fissures and splits which chemical cleaning agents may enter and from which it may be difficult to rinse the chemicals.

A wide range of sandstones have been used as building stone through-out the UK. It is essential that each type is identified or classified before the initial selection of cleaning methods for on-site trials is made. The publication *Sandstones of the British Isles* is a useful reference for initial identification.[10] Petrographic analysis will be necessary to identify details of constituents, properties and weathering.

Soiling versus patina

The colour of historic, soiled sandstone is the result of two mechanisms: colour changes from within the stone, known as patina and matter which has been deposited on the stone surface, known as soiling. The purpose of a cleaning operation should be to remove the applied soiling only and not the staining which is integral to the surface of the stone. The integral staining may not always be continuous and can cause a cleaned surface to appear patchy, as demonstrated in the second example in this section.

The sandstones of Glasgow

During 1991–92, Dr Brian Bluck of the Department of Geology and Applied Geology at the University of Glasgow, and Jane Porter, a stone sculpture conservator of the Burrell Museum in Glasgow published and presented their findings on the characteristics of two sandstones widely used in the city of Glasgow, the modes of deterioration affecting these and the effects of chemical cleaning on their surfaces.[11–13]

The red sandstone, one of the red Permian rocks of the south of Scotland, had a high porosity and comprised mainly silica grains and iron oxide coating. The blonde sandstone, a carboniferous of either local or northern England origin, was made up of silica cemented by carbonate, clays and iron oxide and had a lower porosity than the red sandstone. Through natural weathering processes, the red sandstone developed a dark red patina of iron oxide while the blonde sandstones developed a brown-yellow patina of iron oxides, carbohydrates and clays. The patina on the blonde sandstone was thicker, more variable and often less permeable than that on the red due to the stone's greater proportion of unstable minerals. The Bluck and Porter work described

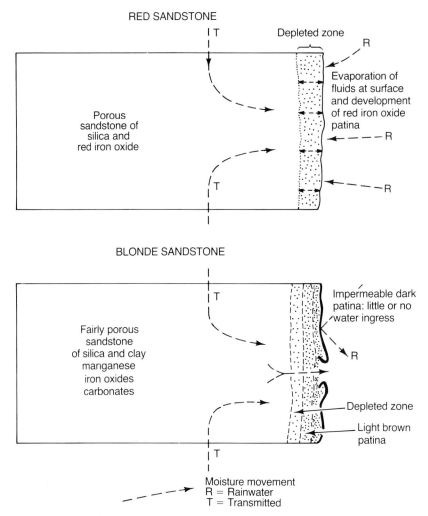

Figure 4.3 The ingress–egress cycle, the build-up of patina and the sources of moisture for the two sandstones commonly used in Glasgow buildings, as presented by Bluck and Porter. (From Bluck and Porter (1991), p.21.)

the development of the natural patina of these sandstones, establishing it as inherent to the stone and differentiating it from soiling which has impinged on the surface from the atmosphere.

Residual soiling on cleaned sandstone

Following the cleaning of the external masonry of the Church of St John the Evangelist in Edinburgh, areas of grey-black soiling were found on the very light-coloured sandstone. The alkaline poultice and liquid acidic chemicals used to undertake the general cleaning procedures did not affect these residual areas of discolouration. Architects for the project, Gray, Marshall & Associates, commissioned independent analysis to determine the nature of the staining and whether it would be possible to remove it without damage.[14]

The surfaces affected by the staining appeared to be sound and without scaling or granulation. In the building context, the extent and intensity of the staining was not uniform but appeared to be related to areas of heavier water loading. The research aimed to establish whether the grey-black colour was the stone's patina or residual atmospheric soiling.

Petrological examination revealed the soiling to be an almost mono-mineralic layer one or two grains thick with an interstitial infill of opaque material. Microscopic investigation of broken sections of stone indicated the soiling layer to be located beneath a layer of quartz unaffected by the colouring. The samples under investigation revealed little apparent interconnection between the soiling layer and the outer surface of the stone. Extensive chemical and physical analysis was also undertaken. On completion of the analytical work, it was concluded that the soiling was residual atmospheric soiling which had remained due to the mineralogical texture of the stone.

The chemistry of the residual soiling layer did not differ significantly from the chemistry of the general soiling found on the stone surface so its removal was considered possible if the cleaning compound could be brought into contact with the subsurface soiling.

During laboratory cleaning trials it was found that any chemical procedure which was effective in removing the soiling layer and involved the use of water also mobilized the iron content of the stone layer beneath the soiling, meaning that any such procedure would remove the soiling layer under investigation but lead to replacement with another form of discolouration. It was noted that use of mechanical abrasive methods to remove the subsurfaces soiling layer would involve removal of significant depths of stone.

4.2 GRANITE

Granite is a strictly defined rock.[15] It is an acid plutonic igneous rock which has a fairly limited range of composition. The granite family includes members which contain varying proportions of quartz, alkali plagioclase feldspar, potash feldspar and a dark-coloured ferromagnesian

Figure 4.4 One of the groups of massive granite columns supporting the tympanum of the Albert Memorial. All polished granite surfaces are readily damaged by hydrofluoric acid based cleaning agents and many abrasive processes; consequently they must be protected from these if used elsewhere. The cleaning of polished granite requires different materials and procedures from the cleaning of unpolished granite.

mineral, which is generally either biotite mica or hornblende. Other accessory minerals may be present, but never in great amounts, unless as purely local concentrations. Granites contain a high proportion of pale-coloured minerals. Quartz, which must be present, is usually found to be colourless; however, in the main mass of the rock, it appears to be grey, although it may sometimes have a pale purple hue. The dark brown mica, biotite, is evenly scattered throughout the mass and, if the pale-coloured mica, muscovite, is present, it is distinguished by a silvery appearance. The mineral present in the greatest quantity is feldspar. Two varieties of feldspar are common, orthoclase and plagioclase. They may occur together in the same rock, but plagioclase is less common. Orthoclase is usually white to flesh pink but may be red; plagioclase is white to grey or, more rarely, yellowish, brown or pink. Because feldspar makes up the bulk of the rock, this mineral determines the overall colour of the stone.

Syenite is not a common rock in Britain and it is often identified as granite. The original type, which comes from near Dresden, is composed mostly of hornblende and orthoclase feldspar. Syenite is light grey to reddish in colour and is often described as granite without quartz. One particular type, Larvikite, from Norway, has been used in polished form on many UK facades and interiors.

Granites are well known for their durability in many types of environment. At times, granites which are partially kaolinized (breakdown of feldspars) can be found in exterior building contexts. The resultant loss of matrix can lead to a susceptibility to salt crystallization damage. The occurrence of this and other forms of deviation from idealized or expected composition should be allowed for, e.g. calcite may occur as an alteration product but be inherent to the stone.

The cleaning of polished granite surfaces needs to be approached differently from the cleaning of unpolished surfaces as the polish of these surfaces is readily etched by dilute solutions of hydrofluoric acid based cleaners. Unpolished surfaces are often cleaned with these products. They are also tolerant of wet abrasive cleaning procedures. Fine, moderate weight abrasives at low pressures can be very effective. There is usually no need to select a high impact process.

4.3 LIMESTONES AND MARBLES

Limestones

Limestones consist chiefly of calcium carbonate ($CaCO_3$) in the form of the finely divided mineral calcite. Limestones are formed either directly or indirectly from mineral matter dissolved usually, but not always, in sea water and may be made up of as much as 99 per cent calcium carbonate. However, other mineral matter may be present in significant amounts. Limestones are very widespread, particularly in the Midlands and south of the UK. Their natural bedding orientation may or may not be obvious to the eye. They are commonly richly fossiliferous.[16]

Limestones can be classified simply on the basis of their modes of origin:

1. Chemical limestones are formed directly by precipitation of calcium carbonate from water.
2. Organic limestones consist largely or entirely of the fossilized shells of one or more organisms. The organisms removed calcium carbonate from the water in which they lived and used it for their shells or skeletons.
3. Clastic or detrital limestones result from the erosion of pre-existing limestones.

Figure 4.5 The limestone dressings to this church, comprising one of the Bath limestones, have soiled and weathered in a typical manner. Erosion and cleaning have been experienced by surfaces most frequently in contact with rainwater. Unwashed areas, which are also those which are most heavily soiled, are exhibiting breakdown of the sulphated surface that has developed.

When pure, or nearly so, limestones are white in colour. Few limestones, however, are composed entirely of calcium carbonate. Most contain other mineral matter which will determine its overall colour. Clay is one of the commonest non-calcareous constituents of limestone. Many other materials may be present in limestones.

Figure 4.6 Portland limestone viewed from within a fracture running parallel and near to the outer, weathered surface. Much of the calcite binding material is missing from between the oolites and shell fragments. Pollutants can be seen within some voids. (Photographed at ×40, plain polarized light, Lithan Ltd.)

A particularly useful reference on building limestones which are currently available is *The Building Limestones of the British Isles.*[17]

The principal mineral component of magnesian limestones is *dolomite*, a double carbonate of calcium and magnesium ($CaMg(CO_3)_2$). The dolomite may have originated as a chemical deposit but more probably formed by the chemical alteration termed dolomitization. Nearly all the limestones of Permian age in England contain dolomite. In general, dolomitic limestones are more resistant to weathering than pure limestones, but they are particularly vulnerable in heavily polluted atmospheres. Magnesian limestones are also referred to as dolomitic limestones.

The colour can vary from cream to buff or yellow to grey. The level of impurities is mostly very low,, commonly including quartz, calcite, clay and iron oxide. Some of the Nottinghamshire and Derbyshire stones are extremely quartz rich, and for this reason are often regarded as sandstones. The most well known of these is White Mansfield.[18].

Description of the constituents, properties and usage of magnesian limestones can be found in the Building Research Establishment report *The Building Magnesian Limestones of the British Isles*.[19]

Quartz, in the form of sand grains, may also be present, either by itself or in association with other minerals. In rare instances a limestone may be rich in one of the iron minerals, e.g. siderite and chamosite.[20] The complex iron-silicate, *glauconite*, is an occasional constituent of limestones but it is not as widespread in limestone as in sandstones. *Pyrite* (iron disulphide, FeS_2) may be present and in disseminated form contributes to the dark colour of some limestones. *Manganese* minerals, normally in the form of manganite, may have a dramatic effect even when present in small quantities. It appears as attractive dendritic patterns on the joints or bedding-planes, particularly of fine-grained limestones.

Although limestone is not quarried for dimension stone on the same huge scale that it is for crushed rock and for industrial use, it has, nevertheless, contributed greatly and sometimes dramatically to the appearance of many British buildings and towns. Limestones are widely distributed geographically and, like sandstones, are of common occurrence throughout the geological column. They are less common in the older systems, but increase in prominence in younger rocks.

Marble

The terms marble and limestone are wrongly and commonly confused.[21] Limestone is a sedimentary rock. Marble is a metamorphic rock made up mostly of calcite ($CaCO_3$). It is readily attacked by acids. In a marble the calcite is recrystallized to produce an interlocking granular mosaic of similarly sized calcite crystals. Calcite is the name given to calcium carbonate when it is in crystal form. The recrystallization removes any of the original sedimentary structures and fossils. 'The resulting marble is harder and more compact because the pore spaces have been reduced. Pure marble is white; the molting, banding, and colors of ornamental varieties result from impurities... All varieties of marble are soft enough to be easily scratched; it has a hardness of 3.0 on the Mohs scale.'[22]

Weaver warns of the characteristics that marble selected for internal uses may have:

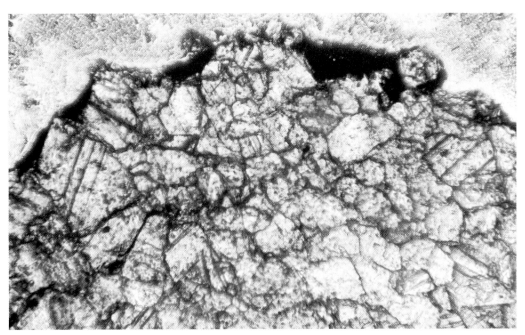

Figure 4.7 Thin section photomicrograph of Carrara marble with a soiled and weathered surface. At this magnification, pollutants not seen with the naked eye are apparent together with the extent of penetration into the mineralogy both through the grains and around their boundaries. Mechanical cleaning procedures applied to this surface would only remove surface soiling. (Photographed at ×60, plain polarized light, Lithan Ltd.)

Despite popular opinion to the contrary, marble although a wonderful material is relatively soft, and thus easily scratched or abraded; easily stained; easily dissolved or etched even by comparatively weak acids; and usually has the unfortunate combination of being both extremely fragile and extremely heavy. It must therefore be treated with extreme care and caution. Some marbles, especially old marbles, may easily be damaged simply by soaking with water.[23]

As marble weathers in the external environment, the bonds between the grains of calcite are loosened and the surface assumes a sugary appearance known as saccharoidal weathering. A limestone and a marble will weather in different ways.

Because of the comparative rarity of marble in the British Isles, as well as its limited range of colour, the geological difficulties of working and the remoteness of the quarries, marble has been imported since at least Roman times. There is little doubt but that much of it was chosen principally for its colour.

Italy claims first place in the production of marble. Without doubt the most widely known locality is Carrara in Tuscany. Greece produces the classic white marbles, Parian and Pentelic, as well as the highly coloured Skyros marble. White Pentelic (or Pentelicon) may be white or may have cloudy markings. The cloudy markings may contain finely disseminated iron pyrites in crystal form. Often the stone has a delicate, soft light golden cast. Marble in the UK may also have come from Ireland, France, Turkey, Norway or Sweden. Significant quantities of marble exist in the United States of America.

Weathering and soiling of limestones and marbles

Limestones and marbles should be considered delicate stones composed of calcium carbonate which is highly sensitive to acids, even acidic rainwater. Particular consideration should be given to those limestones which are softer and more porous than marble. As limestone weathers, its outer zone becomes weaker and more porous and therefore more susceptible to damage during cleaning. A marble or limestone surface of low strength is susceptible to damage by pressure water washing or abrasive cleaning (wet or dry); ones with high porosity are susceptible to absorption of chemicals; their calcium carbonate composition make them susceptible to any acid at all.[24]

Sulphur dioxide (SO_2) dissolves easily in water to form sulphurous acid (H_2SO_3) which is one of the main protagonists in the acid attack of calcareous surfaces, including limestone and marble. Acids derived from sulphur-based gases in the air interact with the calcareous stone to form calcium sulphate which crystallizes as the mineral gypsum ($CaSO_4.2H_2O$). Gypsum is slightly soluble in pure water (and more so in acidic waters), and on portions of limestone facades which are frequently washed by rain, it is removed along with any dirt which has also become affixed to the limestone surface. In these areas, the stone is, in effect, being kept clean by gradual solution weathering.[25]

The story is different in areas which are not washed by rainwater. Here, acidic mists particles react with the limestone surfaces to bind any particulate pollutants present to that surface. As this process develops, the skin formed on the stone becomes less and less permeable and the surface becomes darker as particles of soiling become attached to it. In urban environments where particulate pollution is high, surfaces often become black and display thicknesses of 6–12 mm (0.25–0.5 in.) of encrusted soiling. In areas of low particulate pollution, the stone surface may develop just a brown hue.

Different limestones respond to the virtually impermeable gypsum or sulphated skin which forms on their surfaces in different ways. Coarser-pored, more durable limestones are able to retain their skins without breakdown. On the other hand, sulphate skins on finer-pored limestones tend to form blisters which eventually split to reveal deteriorated, flaking, powdery stone behind.

Sulphate skins also form on the surfaces of *magnesian limestones*. Sulphur-based pollutants which react with their surfaces produce calcium sulphate and magnesium sulphate. The calcium sulphate formed creates a sulphate skin in similar manner to simple limestones. This is penetrated by the magnesium sulphate which is more soluble than gypsum and which crystallizes and recrystallizes in the stonework behind, creating deep caverns of decay which are revealed when the sulphate skin breaks down.[26]

Marbles are chemically similar to limestones and therefore also react to sulphur-based pollutants. In areas which are washed by rain, soiling is unable to accumulate as the marble surface is dissolved and gradually eroded. Sulphate skins form in unwashed areas.

Granulation, flaking and scaling are often evident in association with soiling crusts. On the one hand, the crust itself is not necessarily the cause but rather the effect of some other mechanism such as salt crystallization beneath the surface of the stone. On the other hand, the presence of a soiling crust can hide surface breakdown, the extent of which is not fully revealed until the crust itself falls off or is removed from the surface by cleaning.

Surface crusts, particularly thick ones, have a role in the deterioration of the stone beneath. The extent of this should be determined on a case by case basis as part of a larger analytical programme established to investigate the properties of and other problems related to the stone. Even if an immediate relationship cannot be seen between surface soiling and the deterioration of the stonework beneath, the effect of leaving the existing soiling to develop and thicken must also be assessed. Current criteria for assessing deterioration also need to be adjusted as so often is stone deterioration considered to be under way only when breakdown, which represents the end of a decay process, can be observed with the naked eye.

The bonding of crusts to their calcareous substrate is often strong and the physical relationship between the two is an intimate one. Removing a crust may directly affect the substrate. It may also mean the removal of the original stone surface which is contained within it: a practice which may be unacceptable on historical or archaeological grounds. It is in fact difficult not to affect a substrate during cleaning, and much of the fine tuning undertaken during cleaning operations is aimed principally at reducing the impact of this operation.

Gypsum (calcium sulphate) deposition takes place on other stones, e.g. sandstone, brick and granite which are subject to run-off from limestone and marble. These predominantly non-calcareous materials experience surface breakdown as a result. Analysis will confirm the presence of carbonate and sulphate deposits.

4.4 ALABASTER

Alabaster is a large variety of gypsum which can be found used in monuments, statuary and decorative work in building interiors. The stone is water-soluble. The cleaning of alabaster surfaces is highly specialized work which should be undertaken by stone conservators.

4.5 SLATE

Slates cannot withstand normal cleaning methods. They are susceptible to alteration by hydrofluoric acid (HF) based cleaning products. Gentle air abrasive cleaning can be appropriate at times. Generally, the use of non-ionic soap in warm water, associated brushing and the use of low pressure water rinsing is sufficient.

For further information regarding slates, see the report by Hart.[27]

4.6 BRICKS

Historical brickwork has a wide variety of characteristics and variables. While bricks are made mainly from clay earth and are fired in kilns, the variety of clay types, manufacturing and firing processes and resultant characteristics of colour and surface texture is vast. The history of brickmaking in the UK began with the Romans and has continued since that time. Most brick types are porous, and most are susceptible to impact damage. Chemical cleaning must always be undertaken with caution. The fireskin on bricks should not be affected by cleaning processes. Traditional brickwork pointing mortars which were based on soft mixes of lime and sand and are usually even softer than the bricks themselves should also not be damaged.

Figure 4.8 A wide range of hardnesses are present in this eighteenth century brickwork. Its lime-rich mortar is very soft and weathered but remains sound. Variations of this magnitude are not uncommon on historical brickwork, nor are heavily textured or profiled surfaces. They explain the ease with which such surfaces are damaged by abrasive cleaning methods. Flintwork at the base of this wall with the vast contrast in hardness between flints and sand/lime mortar poses even greater problems as regards cleaning. Fortunately, none of these surfaces requires cleaning.

When brickwork is to be cleaned the following variables must be considered:

1. The variety of colour, texture and degree of firing that can be found within one brick wall and the corresponding variety in degree and tenacity of soiling.

2. The effect of surface texture. Highly textured surfaces include convolutions and are easily damaged by abrasive cleaning which attempts to remove soiling from crevices and pores. The cleaning of engineering bricks will be a different operation from the cleaning of bricks hand-made in earlier centuries. Smooth-faced brickwork is susceptible to streaking during chemical cleaning processes due to runs of liquid cleaner. Liquid cleaners must be applied evenly, working bottom to top in a cleaning area, and brickwork beneath an area being cleaned needs to be wetted prior to rinsing off of the chemical cleaner above.

3. The softness of certain brick types, e.g rubbers and under-fired, less vitrified individual bricks, and their ability to withstand abrasive cleaning methods, including manual brushing.

4. The high porosity of bricks generally and the probability of a high range of porosities on a brick-by-brick basis.

5. The susceptibility of harder, engineering-type bricks to impact damage and hence abrasive cleaning, and to the misuse of HF-based cleaning acids.

6. The sensitivity or resistivity of heavy soiling on some brick surfaces to hydrofluoric acid-based chemical cleaners, for example, London Stocks and Norfolk Whites.

7. The high sensitivity of glazed bricks to etching by hydrofluoric acid-based cleaners and damage by abrasive cleaning processes. Neither should be used.

8. The use of dyes in nineteenth century brickwork to achieve even colouring throughout bricks, and the sensitivity of such dyes to chemical cleaning agents.

9. Victorian patterned brickwork may contain bricks of several colours and hardnesses. These will have different sensitivities to both chemical and abrasive cleaning processes.

10. The high percentage of joints in the surface area of a brick wall. In pre-nineteenth century brickwork this can be as high as 30 per cent, requiring the cleaning process to be equally suitable to the cleaning of the mortar surface as the bricks themselves.

11. The comparative softness of sand and lime mortar compared with associated brickwork.

12. The presence of special joint profiles, for example tuck pointing, the tuck typically being composed of pure lime.

13. The presence of oxide washes applied to brickwork surfaces to unify their appearance and the effect of the selected cleaning process on these.

14. Associated remedial works such as removal of cementitious patch repairs used to build up weathered arrises or areas of heavily deteriorated brickwork.

Bricks vary considerably in their tendency to soil and decay. The least vulnerable are those which are dense, vitrified or semi-vitrified or which have a vitrified surface finish. Highest risks are to gauged ('rubbing') bricks.

The high ratio of mortar to brick surface area in all but very fine jointed work, sometimes makes a significant contribution to the soiling pattern. Lime deposits in the form of a white film and light patches of efflorescence are common. Marked damage can often be seen under limestone dressings where there is no drop or water check, and many bricks deteriorate in sheltered zones under protective mouldings or copings where they are not washed by the rain.

Any cleaning method on brickwork involving water alone can only be expected to remove superficial or loosely adherent dirt (unless excessively high pressures are used). Water cannot break the siliceous bond by which remaining soiling adheres. The same applies to the use of non-ionic soaps. Damage can easily take place if associated brushing is undertaken using brushes with bristles which are too harsh, too coarse or used too vigorously.

Periods of saturation associated with pre-wetting and rinsing of chemical cleaning and even with wet abrasive cleaning easily lead to the emergence of efflorescence. The water has the effect of dissolving inherent or introduced salts within the brick surface, bringing them to the surface during the drying-out process. The efflorescence should be dry-brushed or vacuumed from the wall surface taking care to ensure the salts are collected and not allowed to redeposit elsewhere on the masonry. (See Chapter 5, Volume 2, for more detailed information.)

Abrasive cleaning systems are frequently inappropriate on historic brickwork, unless undertaken extremely carefully with a level of skill not often found in the cleaning industry. The uniformity of approach of abrasive methods is unable to deal with the multitude of variations that can be present in a brick wall, as listed above. They are at times appropriate as adjuncts to other cleaning systems, for example, the removal of loosely adherent limewash.

Chemical cleaning is a widely used approach for brickwork as it is able to accommodate variations in texture, condition and hardness. For heavy soiling, cleaning can involve an alkali-based agent followed by an agent containing hydrofluoric acid or, if soiling is lighter, by the acidic agent alone. The brick surfaces must be thoroughly pre-wetted to limit the activity of cleaning agents to the surface. Thorough rinsing of the surface is also critical. Rinse pressures must not be excessive and encourage the cutting out of weathered sand and lime joints, a frequent problem associated with chemical cleaning. Acidic cleaning formulations used for cleaning bricks will readily dissolve lime-based mortars.

Chemicals should be applied by brush. Reduced concentrations of chemical agents are frequently more effective than initially supposed. It is also possible to achieve excellent results with short dwell times. This will, of course, require work areas of reduced size which may in turn extend the time required for a project. This should not be of concern provided the need for it is established prior to the tendering process.

Proprietary hydrofluoric acid formulations incorporating the rust inhibitor, orthophosphoric acid, are usually recommended to reduce the risk of brown staining emanating from mortar aggregates which are affected by the acid. This may not be necessary if the standard acid cleaner is used at short dwell time and/or in diluted form. Hydrochloric acid-based cleaners are best avoided.

Plain clay tiles

Plain clay tiles on roofs and walls can be cleaned in the same manner as unglazed brickwork, taking heed of all the same precautions.

4.7 TERRACOTTA AND FAIENCE

Characteristics and usage

Terracotta and faience are fired clay products. Their clays vary in colour from red and brown to dark grey and off-white. The wet clays are mixed with other materials such as sand, and crushed, previously fired, ceramic material known as grog is added to control shrinkage while drying and during kiln firing.

Manufacturers in the UK use the term 'terracotta' to describe all unglazed units and 'faience' to describe all glazed units. Another terminology common in the UK uses 'terracotta' to refer to structural units (glazed or unglazed) and 'faience' to refer to cladding units (glazed or unglazed). Use of the term 'faience' dates only from the mid-twentieth century. Details on the history, manufacture and characteristics of glazed and unglazed terracotta can be found in Berryman and Tindall,[28] Weaver and Matero,[29], and Ashurst.[30]

Terracotta is not always readily identifiable due to the camouflage effect of its surface colour and texture, applied to make it look like another building material such as marble or granite.

In England, terracotta was manufactured and used by the Romans, although little survives from these times or the late fifteenth and early sixteenth centuries when Nonsuch Palace, Sutton Place (1523–27) and

Figure 4.9 The sixteenth century terracotta of Sutton Place, near Guildford, Surrey, has much greater variations in colour, durability and surface finish than those produced in the nineteenth and twentieth centuries. The cleaning, repair and conservation of these surfaces has been undertaken in recent years by conservators.

Hampton Court (c.1520) were constructed. The terracotta of these buildings is distinctly different in external character and, at times, in durability from terracotta's more standardized manufacture of 1840–1910. Prominent nineteenth century buildings constructed of terracotta are the Henry Cole Wing of the Victoria and Albert Museum (1866), the Royal Albert Hall (1867–81) and the Natural History Museum (1880–1905). The Royal Albert Hall still retains identifiable marks of the wet abrasive method used to clean it during the 1970s and the permanent streaks to the exterior of the Natural History Museum are frequently cited as a bad example of high strength hydrofluoric-based acid cleaning on terracotta surfaces. The Henry Cole Wing remains (1993) heavily soiled, blotchy and uncleaned.

In the US, glazed architectural terracotta is probably one of the largest, if not the largest, constituent material in some of the urban environments.[31]

The following products are a range of the most common types of terracotta and faience that will be found in late nineteenth and early twentieth century buildings. Coadestone is a proprietary off-white form of terracotta fired at approximately 1000°C, vitrified and highly durable material. Carraraware was thought to resemble Carrara marble because of its satin finish white glaze. Doultonware is a salt-glazed stoneware fired once at very high temperature. The outer surface of encaustic tiles comprises a slab of very pure clay of selected colour. The cleaning of each material must be approached with extreme caution.

Susceptibilities

Both glazed and unglazed surfaces soil most heavily in areas of heaviest water saturation. Soiling is commonly located at the edges of blocks in the vicinity of mortar joints. Similar to sandstone and brickwork, much of the soiling is not water-soluble and cannot be removed using water alone. While the soiling may be intense in blackness, it is usually fine and in a thin layer. Encrustations build up in protected areas.

The thin fireskin on the outer surface of unglazed terracotta and faience units is particularly sensitive to both chemical and abrasive cleaning. At times, unglazed units were finished with a slip stain, a thin watery paste of clay of different colour from the underbody, applied prior to firing. This is similarly susceptible. Applied glazes are thin, vitreous, transparent or coloured coatings of glassy consistency which are highly sensitive to damage by abrasive and hydrofluoric acid-based chemical cleaning.

It must be remembered during all cleaning operations on terracotta and faience that the maintenance of fire skin, slip stain and glazed

Figure 4.10 The unglazed terracotta facades of Harrods, Knightsbridge have been cleaned on several occasions and bear the evidence of this. Often, terracotta which has been cleaned before reveals the permanent damage of a previous process undertaken when knowledge of the damage caused by incorrect use of alkaline, hydrofluoric acid-based cleaners and abrasive cleaning methods was not widespread. In the 1990s this is no longer an excuse.

surfaces is critical to the historical value and future well-being of the clay body beneath.

The surfaces of terracotta and faience are amongst the easiest historical masonry materials to clean incorrectly. Serious problems can be caused with abrasive cleaning methods, acid and alkali cleaning methods, and mechanical cleaning methods including metal brushes. However, their surfaces can be successfully cleaned with chemical cleaning methods but only if used with extreme caution at exceedingly low concentrations and always under a high level of continuing supervision.

Abrasive cleaning readily pits and scores unglazed and glazed terracotta surfaces. When used on unglazed surfaces the fire skin may easily be broken down or completely removed if aggregate types and pressures suitable for some sandstones are used. Irregularities in surface colouring produced in the kiln can be easily removed by even the finest, lowest impact abrasive process. The successful cleaning of unglazed terracotta by abrasive means requires the use of extremely fine particles at low particle flow and demands a very high consistent standard of workmanship from operatives and supervisors who have a thorough understanding of the nature of the surface and the soiling. It is so rarely that this is achieved in practice that both wet and dry abrasive methods are usually best avoided. Unless undertaken by trained conservators with pencil abrasive equipment on localized areas of soiling, they are not recommended.

The chemical cleaning of unglazed terracotta and faience surfaces relies on hydrofluoric acid to break down the silicates. Until recently, the UK experience of cleaning unglazed terracotta and faience with hydrofluoric acid-based solutions has generally been bad. Reasons for this have been the use of proprietary products which have been too strong, of wrong consistency or used for excessively long dwell times. Poor job management has also been the cause of much residual streaking. It has been discovered that hydrofluoric acid readily attacks all glasses and, therefore, glazing.

Chemical cleaning of glazed surfaces at times requires the use of an alkali degreaser prior to the neutralizing product. Surprisingly good results can be gained with extremely low concentrations of both active ingredients. On unglazed surfaces, their efficiency is greatly improved by agitation during the determined dwell time and/or localized scrubbing using plastic pot scourers or similar. However, alkalis can be very detrimental in the longer term to some glaze compositions designed for low melting point.

Streaking can be avoided by the application of cleaning agents with sponges and agitation of surfaces to prevent the formation of runs during the dwell time. Thixotropic agents also assist in preventing streaking.

The upward-facing or water-saturated surfaces of terracotta facades are usually heavily soiled and frequently require a second application of the determined general cleaning method. The temptation to select a single method which is suited for the cleaning of both lightly and heavily soiled areas in one process should be avoided.

The successful cleaning of unglazed terracotta buildings using chemical agents will depend on well-trained and experienced operatives and virtually constant supervision. The implications of what happens to terracotta surfaces beyond the work area is critical to the overall result.

On glazed surfaces, frequently the use of water (cold or hot), detergent, natural or nylon bristle brushes or plastic pot scourers are a non-damaging way of removing excessive soiling. Acidic chemical cleaners which contain hydrofluoric acid should not be used as they will clean by dissolving the silica of the glaze, leaving an etched and dulled surface.

Cleaning of glazed and unglazed surfaces with non-ionic detergent in warm water and plastic pot scourers will only be successful in removing superficial or loosely adherent soiling. Glazed surfaces soil when particulate matter becomes embedded within fractures within the glaze. This is impossible to remove. Glazed units are most heavily soiled in the vicinity of joints. At times, this can be removed by non-ionic detergent in warm water applied with plastic pot scourers and elbow grease. If this is not successful, it may be necessary to resort to alkaline agents.

4.8 MORTARS AND PLASTERS

Most traditional mortars and renders prior to the nineteenth century were based on non-hydraulic lime and aggregate. As the lime has the same chemical composition as limestone (calcium carbonate, $CaCO_3$), surfaces of plaster and pointing mortars which are lime-based will have soiled and weathered in a manner similar to calcareous stones. Sulphated skins, black crusts and clean surfaces in areas of rinsing will all be present.

On external lime-based renders, the removal of organic growth and defective limewash will be the most frequent cleaning problems experienced. Sand and lime mortars and renders are frequently softer

Figure 4.11 Organic soiling on late-sixteenth century sand/lime plaster, which has been exposed to the weather for nearly four centuries, in the process of being removed by toothbrushes and hand spatulas.

than the stone or brick they surround and can easily be damaged if cleaned by abrasive methods or pressure water which is being used on the masonry units nearby. They are readily dissolved by hydrochloric and hydrofluoric acids. Sand and lime mortars and renders are very porous, usually far more so than their surrounding masonry; they are, therefore, more susceptible to absorption and retention of cleaning chemicals.

A very light level of abrasive clean with fine particles can at times be appropriate for the removal of the residues of loose or flaking paint or limewash prior to recoating. The use of an alkaline paint remover may lead to unwanted deposition of soluble salts. Any chemical which will soften and dissolve the limewash will do the same to the surface of the render beneath. Hand brushing to remove organic soiling is not generally recommended as damage is readily caused to the soft plaster surfaces beneath. In rare exceptions, the use of soft, crinkle wire, phosphor bronze brushes or natural bristle brushes can be successful when used extremely lightly.

In the late eighteenth and nineteenth centuries, a great deal of quality building in London was undertaken in stucco, to the designs of the

Adam brothers, John Nash, James and Samuel Wyatt to mention a very few. Throughout that time, four broad types of mortar were available:

1. Lime-sand.
2. Oil-based compositions.
3. Hydraulic lime-based (predominantly Roman cement).
4. Portland cement-based.

Roman cement was patented in 1796 and Portland cement in 1824. Pointing mortars in these materials will also be found on facades built or repaired during this time. Most stucco in these materials was intended from the beginning to be coloured. Initially this took the form of colour washing, or more expensively, frescoing in imitation of stone:

> The temporary nature of colour washing and the expense of frescoing meant that eventually stucco came to be oil-painted. But although there are one or two references in the 1820s and 1830s which suggest that oil painting was used, it seems not to have become general until the 1840s.[32]

Today, many stucco buildings in the London area have layers of oil-based paint in the vicinity of 6 mm (0.25 in.) thick. As the earliest coat was often applied over the powdery surface of weathered limewash, intercoat adhesion at this level is poor. The weight of the oil-based paint has served to pull it away from much of the wall surface. Damp has managed to penetrate fractures in the paint and has caused predictable damp-related deterioration problems. In many instances, painting over the existing substrate has been recognized as a waste of money and the problem of removing the copious coating layers has begun to be addressed.

A thick build-up of oil-based paint is frequently more brittle and hard than the render beneath. Cleaning by abrasive or pressure water means is rarely acceptable because of the damage caused to the render beneath. Successful projects have involved the combination of methods such as hot air (not flame burning) followed by mild, wet abrasive or paint removing poultices and associated low pressure rinsing. In each instance, an extended period of on-site trials was necessary.

The important issues of collection of lead-based residues for disposal is discussed in Chapter 7, Volume 2.

4.9 CAST STONE (ARTIFICIAL STONE)

Cast or artificial stone units are manufactured in moulds, out of mortars composed of various aggregates and binding media of cement, lime and other additives.

Cast stone can be cleaned using water-based methods. Differential erosion can be caused if the impact of pressure water is too great. Where water cleaning is ineffective, air abrasion or treatment with chemical agents, based on hydrochloric acid (HCl) may be used. However, it must be recognized that several constituents of cast stone are acid-sensitive. Some types of cast stone are highly porous and prone to absorption of chemical agents.

Resistance to damage as the result of air abrasive and pressure water cleaning will depend on the constituents and details of manufacturing. Some artificial stones are highly susceptible. In others, differences in surface compaction and hardness can result in localized losses.

Soiling can have a high component of organic growth. In these instances, low pressure water and mild wet abrasive processes are usually most effective.

4.10 ASSOCIATED MATERIALS

The cleaning or protection of small areas of other materials associated with masonry walling must receive special attention as most can be incompatible with the processes and materials to be used around them.

Heavily weathered and missing sections of pointing can provide entry points for cleaning products and water. Such areas must be blocked before cleaning.

Metals, wood and paints can all be affected by several commercially available cleaning procedures and products. Technical literature and preliminary testing should indicate the type of protection these will require.

Loose paint will be removed when latex protective materials and masking tapes are stripped at the end of a cleaning job. Trees, shrubs and ground vegetation may also need to be identified for special protection when chemical or abrasive cleaning is undertaken. Particularly important garden areas may need to be transplanted while cleaning is under way and replanted when the associated dangers of trampling, poisoning, burning and shredding have passed.

It is best to consider wood used in buildings as fibrous, porous and extremely sensitive to abrasive cleaning. The difference in hardness within the structural grain is high, with areas of softer wood between the lines of the grain being far more easily damaged than the grain lines themselves. Abrasive cleaning frequently leaves uneven surfaces which can only be restored to smoothness by extensive hand sanding. The removal of paint from wood is included in the next chapter.

The metals bronze, aluminium, lead, copper and zinc are extremely susceptible to denting and pitting by abrasive cleaning and to chemical cleaners both acidic and alkaline. Wrought ironwork is also a relatively soft metal whose surfaces can be reworked with certain abrasives at relatively low pressure. Cast iron, on the other hand, is more able to accept abrasive cleaning of its surfaces without damage. The cleaning of iron, lead and bronze is included in Chapter 5 (this volume) as these metals often feature in architecture and structural elements associated with masonry buildings. Materials and processes for masonry cleaning should not be employed on them.

REFERENCES

1. Spry, A.H. (1982) *Principles of Cleaning Masonry Buildings*, Technical Bulletin 3.1. Melbourne: Australian Council of National Trusts, and National Trust of Australia (Victoria), pp.5–6.
2. Ibid., p.6.
3. Honeyborne, D.B. (1990) Weathering and decay of masonry, *Conservation of Building and Decorative Stone*. London: Butterworth/Heinemann, Volume 1, p.156.
4. The geological material in this section has been extracted principally from:
   Ashurst, J. and Dimes, F.G. (eds) (1990) *Conservation of Building and Decorative Stone*, London: Butterworth/Heinemann, Volume 1, pp.38, 61–62, 86, 88–89, 145–149.
   Honeyborne, D.B. (1990) op. cit., pp.153–178.
5. Ashurst, J. and Dimes, F.G. (eds) (1990) *Conservation of Building and Decorative Stone*, London: Butterworth/Heinemann, Volume 2, p.62.
6. Ibid., Volume 1, p.62.
7. Ibid., Volume 1, p.62.
8. Ibid., Volume 1, p.86.
9. Honeyborne, D.B. (1990) op. cit., p.157.
10. Leary, E. (1986) *The Building Sandstones of the British Isles*, Building Research Establishment Report. London: HMSO.
11. Bluck, B.J. and Porter, J. (1991) Sandstone buildings and cleaning problems, *Stone Industries*, March, pp.21–27.
12. Bluck, B.J. and Porter, J. (1991) Aims and methods of sandstone cleaning, *Stone Industries*, April, pp.21–28.
13. Bluck, B. (1992) The composition and weathering of sandstone in relation to cleaning, *Stone Cleaning and the Nature, Soiling and Decay Mechanisms of Stone*, Proceedings of the International Conference held in Edinburgh, UK, 14–16 April 1992. London: Donhead, pp.125–127.

14. Lithan Ltd (1991) *Analysis of Residual Staining. The Church of St John the Evangelist, Edinburgh*, study prepared for and referred to with the permission of Gray Marshall and Associates, Architects, Edinburgh. Funded by the Scottish Development Agency, Glasgow.
15. Ashurst, J. and Dimes, F.G. (1990) op. cit., Volume 1, p.38.
16. Ashurst, J. and Dimes, F.G. (1990) op. cit., Volume 1, pp.86–89.
17. Leary, E. (1983) *The Building Limestones of the British Isles*, Building Research Establishment Report. London: HMSO.
18. Hart, D. (1988) *The Building Magnesian Limestones of the British Isles*, Building Research Establishment Report. London: HMSO, p.2.
19. Hart, D. (1988), ibid., p.2.
20. Ashurst, J. and Dimes, F.G. (1990) op. cit., Volume 1, p.89.
21. Ashurst, J. and Dimes, F.G. (1990) op. cit., Volume 1, pp.144–149.
22. Waite, J.G. and Cheng, R.J. (1983), A case study of the cleaning and conservation of marble at the Schenectady, New York, City Hall, *Cleaning Stone and Masonry*, a symposium sponsored by ASTM Committee E-6 on Performance of Building Constructions, Louisville, Kentucky, 18 April 1983. Philadelphia: ASTM Publications, p.110.
23. Weaver, M.E. (1993) *Cleaning and Conserving Decorative Interior Marblework*, paper presented at the Interiors Conference for Historic Buildings II, Washington D.C., February 17–19, p.19.
24. Spry, A.H. (1982), op. cit, p.7.
25. Honeyborne, D.B. (1990), op. cit., p.157.
26. Ibid, p.157.
27. Hart, D. (1991) *The Building Slates of the British Isles*, Building Research Establishment Report. London: HMSO.
28. Berryman, N.D. and Tindall, Susan M. (1984) *Terra Cotta: Preservation of an Historic Building Material*. Landmarks Preservation Council of Illinois, USA.
29. Weaver, M.E. with Matero, F.G. (1993) *Conserving Buildings: A Guide to Techniques and Materials*. New York: John Wiley.
30. Ashurst, J. and N. (1988) *Practical Building Conservation: English Heritage Technical Handbook*, Volume 2, *Brick, Terracotta and Earth*. Aldershot: Gower Technical Press.
31. Tiller, D.P. (1979) *The Preservation of Historic Glazed Architectural Terra-Cotta: Preservation Briefs 7*, Technical Preservation Services Division, Heritage Conservation and Recreation Service. Washington: US Government Printing Office, p.2.
32. Kelsall, F. (1988) Stucco, Paper given at a conference organized by the Survey of London at the Society of Antiquaries on 21 October 1988, edited by Hermione Hobhouse and Ann Saunder. Royal Commission on the Historical Monuments of England in Association with the London Topographical Society, Publication No.140, 1989, p.24.

Chapter Five

Cleaning Metals and Timber

Owners and contractors involved in the cleaning of historical masonry are often called to address the cleaning of associated architectural features made of timber, iron, bronze and lead. This chapter includes a description of the properties of each of these materials and suitability of cleaning methods which are frequently used on them. For further details, the references indicated should be consulted.

5.1 CLEANING AND SURFACE PREPARATION OF HISTORICAL IRONWORK*

The cleaning of iron usually involves the removal of paint and rust. The purpose of the work is to prepare a sound, clean surface for a subsequent paint system or to reveal the true condition of the iron prior to repair. Specifications for the cleaning and repair of iron must be integrated.

Wrought iron and cast iron are the two most common forms of ironwork that will be encountered in historic buildings. Mild steel may be original to constructions from the late nineteenth century on or a

---

* The material in this section was first published in *Practical Building Conservation: English Heritage Technical Handbook*, Volume 4, *Metals* by Nicola Ashurst and John Ashurst (Aldershot: Gower Technical Press, 1988).

Figure 5.1 Wrought iron railings and balconies are an important feature of Regency architecture in England. Many years of neglect will make their conservation and repair an expensive operation which, in instances such as this, requires the assembly to be removed to the workshop so that the appropriate cleaning and repair work can be undertaken. This will involve treatment of the embedded ends of bars. When the balcony is refixed, stone indent repairs will be required to the wall surface.

substitute material used in repairs. Descriptions of usage and associated construction details may be found in several references and are not investigated here.[1]

Types of iron

Wrought iron, cast iron and steel have properties in common but several differentiating properties which are important in determining which method of cleaning is most suitable.

Wrought iron is the purest form of iron with less than 1 per cent carbon. It performs well in tension but is nevertheless relatively soft and malleable, making it susceptible to surface damage and reworking by abrasive and other mechanical cleaning methods. Wrought iron can be worked hot or cold. It is able to sustain the rapid heat changes associated with traditional flame cleaning. In both architectural and structural detailing, wrought iron frequently includes crevices and recesses and areas which are prone to corrosion and can only really be satisfactorily reached by the flame cleaning process. The problem of toxic fumes from lead-based paints needs to be addressed.

Cast iron is an alloy of iron and carbon (up to 5 per cent). The most common traditional form is grey cast iron. This cannot be forged or worked mechanically either hot or cold. The crystalline structure of cast iron makes it relatively brittle and weak in tension. The material is most successfully cleaned by abrasive methods.

Steel is more tolerant of abrasive cleaning than wrought iron but can nevertheless be similarly affected. Flame cleaning of difficult junctions can complement the use of an abrasive process.

The function of traditional paint on iron

Cast iron and wrought iron were painted primarily for protection against corrosion and secondarily for decorative effect. A build-up of layers was necessary to isolate the metal from its environment. Each coat of paint had a specific purpose.

The primary coat could include any of the following:

♦ Red lead, a bright orange oxide of lead, also known as minium or orange mineral, has been in use as a protective pigment for over two thousand years and has the effect of inhibiting the rust-forming reaction. Removal or disturbance of this coating has health, safety and environmental implications. Today its re-application is limited to listed historical buildings for which exemption has been given through the Society for the Protection of Ancient Buildings.

♦ Iron oxide, the natural and most stable form of iron, is a reddish or brownish pigment. Although it was ubiquitous in nineteenth-century primers, iron oxide had little rust-inhibiting effect. (The chemical basis for oxidation and the chemistry of paint were only partially understood during the nineteenth century.)

♦ Zinc dust came into general use as a protective pigment in the early nineteenth century. Today 'zinc rich' coatings are considered amongst the best protective treatments available.

♦ Linseed oil was a common binding agent of these protective pigments.

♦ Pitch and bitumen had no anti-corrosive chemical properties but were used widely to form a reasonably dependable waterproof coating on structures such as bridges.

The intermediate coats or undercoats were applied to build up thickness and make it difficult for moisture or air to pass through the coatings. The finish coat of paint provided the first line of defence against the environment and determined the final appearance of the iron. Today the same principles of painting iron apply. The various coats within a painting system must, of course, be compatible with one another.

In interior locations, ironwork was often protected simply by the application of oils or waxes or less complex paint systems. A traditional treatment for internal wrought iron was to scrape, chip, or pickle the surface until all scale and foreign substances were removed. A heavy coat of linseed oil was applied, then the iron was heated, and wiped over with emery cloth. Finally, a combination of beeswax and boiled linseed oil was rubbed into the surface. Items treated in this way were sometimes used externally, with the final preparation described being applied annually. Another annual coating sometimes given to internal iron was varnish or shellac. Goose fat with lamp black is another treatment known to have been applied to wrought iron door furniture in both internal and external positions.

Paint analysis

The analysis of paint layers on ironwork should be part of a preparation and repainting programme. The analysis should be approached in a systematic way and undertaken by a person with experience in this field. Samples for microscopic analysis should be carefully removed by scalpel or gentle impact from protected areas which are representative of all coatings which have been applied. Where a less detailed analysis is appropriate, paint layers can be removed in sequence by rubbing with fine wet and dry carborundum paper, lubricated with water or liquid paraffin (mineral oil), or by careful applications of a paint stripper. Alternatively, a chip removed can be inspected under field microscope.

The need for good surface preparation for painting

Correct surface preparation is the most important single factor in the success or failure of a painting operation. Even the best paints or coatings may fail on a badly prepared surface, whilst the simplest and cheapest paint may perform well on a correctly prepared surface. Good surface preparation is essential for good adhesion. To achieve this the new paint must wet the prepared surface, and be applied to a firm, stable foundation.

Specific contaminants to be removed

The preparation of a sound surface usually involves removal of old paint, rust, loose mill scale, grease and soluble corrosion salts. It must be remembered that paint removal may reveal cracks, corrosion and casting defects which were not previously visible. Allowance should therefore be made at the outset for dealing with these.

Old paint
All paint which is loose, perished or flaking must be removed. It is not normally necessary to remove all previous paint coatings if these are sound, hard and firmly adherent and are known to be conventional drying oil paint types, unless a sophisticated modern paint is to be applied, e.g. two-pack epoxide resins. Sound paint surfaces may simply be rubbed down and refinished with one or two suitable coats. Water-based processes such as rubbing and wet abrasive should be used because of the risk from dust from lead pigments. Rubbing down should remove residual gloss, surface deposits and blemishes from previous applications. Operatives and the environment must be properly protected throughout this operation.

Chipped areas of paintwork can be similarly rubbed down, ensuring that the surface under the paint surrounding the chip, to which corrosion has spread, is also cleaned. Locally damaged paint areas should receive a shallow feathered edge, but it can be difficult to achieve a visually acceptable repair by this method to chips in surfaces which comprise multiple layers of paint. New paint coatings should overlap at least 50 mm onto existing sound surrounding paint coatings, and their paint type must be compatible with the existing coatings.

Small areas of paint can be removed with thixotropic chemical paint strippers. Their residues must be removed by white spirit or water, as appropriate. Flame cleaners and hot air blowers which are effective removers of thick layers of paint will produce lead vapours which must not be inhaled. They must be used with care on thin cast iron because of the thermal stresses which can be set up by localized overheating.

Rust

Rust is an unsatisfactory base for paint and must be removed before protective coatings are applied. Rust which remains provides a source of further corrosion beneath new paint surfaces unless it is stabilized. Thin layers of rust can be treated with one of several rust converters. While thorough cleaning is preferable and normally recommended, rust converters are also useful where corroded junctions cannot be taken apart and cleaned properly.

'Flash rusting' will occur on surfaces which are cleaned by processes including water or where dew or condensation form on surfaces cleaned by dry methods. To avoid flash rusting, the final rinse of water-based cleaning methods should include a rust inhibitor. Dry-cleaned surfaces should be primed within one or two hours.

Mill scale (wrought iron and steel)

Mill scale is formed as the result of the hot rolling of wrought iron and steel. As the sections leave the mill rolls they cool and the surface oxidizes, producing mill scale. Mill scale is a non-metallic, brittle surface which is easily damaged and tends to detach from the underlying metal. As rust can form at the break in the scale and spread sideways between it and the metal, loose or defective mill scale must be removed. However, there is evidence to suggest that wrought iron receives corrosion protection from sound, adherent mill scale. For this reason flame cleaning is the preferred treatment for cleaning wrought iron, as it will remove only loose mill scale.

Soluble corrosion salts

Ferrous sulphate and ferrous chloride are undesirable water soluble salts which must be removed from the bottom of pits within an iron surface. They are not readily removed by cleaning with abrasive particles. Tests for soluble corrosion salts should be carried out on iron structures in marine and industrial environments both after cleaning and immediately prior to painting. On-site testing for sulphates and chlorides, the most likely candidates, can be undertaken using test strips. The determination achieved is semi-quantitative and more than adequate as a guide to the amount of sulphate or chloride ions present.

Methods of preparing iron surfaces

Degreasing

Any oil or grease should be removed to avoid subsequent preparation methods spreading the contamination over a wider surface. Large quantities should be physically removed by scraping. The rest is best removed by warm water and detergent followed by thorough water rinsing. Non-caustic degreasing agents are also available, although a wipe over with white spirit and a succession of clean swabs often suffices.

Manual preparation

The simplest form of surface preparation of iron involves chipping, scraping and brushing with hand-held implements. While a surface prepared in this way may appear burnished and clean, only about 30 per cent removal of rust and scale may be achieved. Scoring of valuable surfaces and loss of detail may also occur. Manual preparation may be useful at times in external situations as the first stage in inspection of a heavily corroded item where alternative methods are not available. A corrosion-inhibiting primer such as red lead, zinc phosphate or zinc chromate should be used if this technique is selected. (See page 121 regarding restrictions on the use of red lead.)

Mechanical preparation

These processes involve use of power-driven tools such as grinders and rotary wire brushes. When removing rust, a marginal improvement in cleaning efficiency over manual preparation can be achieved. Rust or other deposits in pits and crevices are rarely removed.

Needle guns, however, can be used more successfully to remove rust and scale, which are broken up and loosened by the impact of a head of iron needles. They can reach into corners and angles inaccessible to other equipment but undesirable residues may still be left in pits and crevices. Needle guns are more appropriately used on cast iron than wrought iron.

Flame cleaning

An oxyacetylene or oxypropane flame is passed across the iron. Arc welding equipment should not be used as the temperature of the flame is too high. Both rust and loose mill scale quickly detach from the iron as the result of differential thermal movement. Immediately after the passage of the flame any loose mill scale, rust and dust that remains is removed by wire brushing. The removal of paint by this method generates toxic fumes and requires the use of masks by operatives.

Flame cleaning is the most efficient and effective method for removing paint, loose mill scale and rust from wrought iron. On a large iron structure, though, it can be slow work. On the other hand, this method enables wrought structures to be examined carefully during cleaning for deterioration, missing elements and inappropriate past repairs. Furthermore, it is very effective at removing loose scale and rust from localized areas such as water traps behind scrolls, and within leafwork, which most other cleaning methods cannot reach.

Thin sections of wrought iron of less than 2 mm may warp during flame cleaning unless the method is used with care. Flame cleaning can be undertaken on site as the equipment is mobile. It can be used under quite wet and damp conditions and helps to dry the surface. The method is, however, a fire hazard and if the flame is traversed too slowly, unbonded scale and other foreign matter may be fused to the surface.

Flame cleaning is often used to 'flash clean' an iron surface of any corrosion which may have developed in the time following cleaning and prior to the application of the primer. It can also be used to create a dry surface for the primer on small sections.

Acid pickling (rust removal)

Acid pickling entails the immersion of items in a bath of warm, dilute sulphuric or phosphoric acid to dissolve and remove mill scale and rust. The acid does not attack the exposed surface appreciably unless the iron remains in the bath for a long time. On removal from the bath the iron must be thoroughly rinsed with clean water. Phosphoric acid has the additional advantage that the reaction with the iron results in a protective layer of phosphates on the surface (anodic inhibitors). Hydrochloric acid and sodium hydroxide (caustic soda) should not be used as they leave soluble salts within the metallic surface which can initiate or accelerate electrochemical corrosion at a later time.

Acid pickling is essentially a works process because it must be carefully controlled. The bath dimension will determine the size of pieces which can be treated.

Rust-removing solutions
Orthophosphoric acid is the basis of many rust-removing solutions sold in retail outlets. Solutions which are described as 'chemically neutral' are

Figure 5.2 The curved balcony railings to the Elizabeth Room of Belvoir Castle, near Grantham, date from the mid-nineteenth century and are made of cast iron, wrought iron and cast lead. Their conservation and repair was undertaken in 1988 by the Ornamental Smiths Workshop of English Heritage. The railing sections were taken to the workshop. Following the analysis of paint samples, all the paint was removed because of its frequent defects and to enable the true extent of works to be determined and undertaken. (English Heritage)

based on a combination of acid and alkali materials and are available from suppliers of conservation materials. Best results are usually achieved when the corroded item is immersed, as this enables the treatment fully to break the bond between the base metal and the corrosion layer. Several solutions are available in gel form.

The mechanical removal of all loose and thick rust layers is advocated

Figure 5.3 Balcony railings to the Elizabeth Room, Belvoir Castle. The variety of metals present and the intricacies of the design required paint to be removed by chemical means. Railing sections were first placed in a bath of caustic soda since the majority of layers to be removed were oil-based. On completion of removal, each railing section then spent four days in a bath of running water to ensure all salts had been removed.(English Heritage)

before the solutions are applied whenever this is archaeologically acceptable.

Chemical removal of paint

Alkali- and solvent-based paint strippers continue to be used to remove paint from iron. Poultice strippers are particularly effective on thick layers. Further information on the use and effectiveness of chemical paint removers can be found in Chapter 7 (Volume 2).

Traditionally, sections of ironwork were immersed in baths of sodium hydroxide (caustic soda) which softened the full thickness of paint and enabled it to be rinsed off the surface. If it is necessary to remove paint in this way, then following rinsing off of the paint, sections of ironwork should be immersed in a bath of running water for forty-eight hours to remove any soluble salts that have been deposited by the caustic stripper.

Abrasive cleaning

As with stone and brick cleaning, the success of abrasive cleaning of cast iron and wrought iron is highly dependent on careful work by

Figure 5.4 Cast iron surfaces are sufficiently robust to be suited to abrasive removal of paint and corrosion products. Wet abrasive processes are most frequently used as these make the necessary collection of lead-based paint residues and spent abrasive easier than dry systems. Dry abrasive processes are used infrequently because of the hazardous dust they create. The cleaning of cast iron can reveal defects such as casting flaws. Once it has been confirmed that these are not of structural concern, the voids should be filled with an epoxy-based iron filler prior to repainting. (English Heritage)

skilled operatives, the right nozzle, grits, flow rates and work distances.

Abrasive cleaning is an appropriate method for cleaning cast iron. It is also widely used on wrought iron because of the speed and relative cheapness of the process (it is much faster than flame cleaning).

However, due to the softness of wrought iron, the milled or wrought surface can be roughened if the approach is too heavy-handed. In conservation terms, this can be undesirable and an alternative cleaning method should be considered.

Abrasive cleaning of wrought iron requires a different approach from the cleaning of structural steel. The material is softer and needs to be cleaned at a slower pace. Test areas should always be experimented on to determine the correct parameters. It is advisable to start at a pressure of 20 psi (approximately 3 kPa) with a fine grit, usually copper slag. A satisfactory cleaning pressure is not likely to exceed 60–70 psi (8–10 kPa). (All pressures used at working distances of 12 inches or more.)

The use of abrasive cleaning is usually not appropriate on wrought iron which includes fine details such as leaves and scrolls. The pressure will need to be substantially reduced and a smaller nozzle used to ensure these are not damaged. Abrasive cleaning of wrought iron with a surface of high intrinsic value is not recommended as the abrasive particles will tend to 'peen' or rework this. Dry abrasive cleaning produces dust and debris on the surface of the iron which must be removed, preferably by vacuum cleaning, prior to painting.

Abrasively-cleaned surfaces are usually specified in terms of surface cleanliness and surface roughness. BS 4232, Surface Finish of Blast Cleaned Steel for Painting, and Swedish Standard SIS 055900, Pictorial Surface Preparation Standards for Painting Steel Surfaces, should be carefully interpreted before being applied to cast iron and wrought iron.

Wet abrasive cleaning is preferable to dry especially where lead-based paint is to be removed, as the dust problem is avoided and collection of residues is made more easy. Wet abrasive processes are also useful in washing from the surface soluble iron salts such as chlorides and sulphates that form within deep corrosion pits in marine and heavily polluted environments. A nozzle with independent control over air, water and abrasive is essential for quick removal of slurry and good visibility of the work surface. An independent air facility is important for the cleaning out of crevices and ledges and for the removal of excess water on completion of cleaning.

Wet abrasive cleaning may, however, cause unwanted water penetration at junctions. There is a very high risk of flash rusting associated with its use, as discussed below. A water tolerant primer is usually advisable after washing or wet abrasive cleaning.

The removal of paints containing lead should not be undertaken by conventional dry air abrasive means because of problems related to the dust produced and difficulty of collecting removed material.

Some dry air abrasive equipment can be fitted with a suction head. All material removed from the surface is transported by vacuum to collection drums which can be sealed and disposed of in accordance with toxic waste requirements, if lead is involved. However, when this equipment is used, it is not possible to see the surface which is being cleaned, which makes it suitable for use on relatively plain steel or cast iron surfaces (the suction head should not be used on masonry). The additional weight of the head and the vacuum line makes it difficult to use. Cleaning takes place at about 50 per cent of normal open nozzle blasting speed, so use of a suction head must be anticipated to be more expensive than ordinary abrasive cleaning.

For both methods, care must be taken to mask surrounding surfaces. All caulking which is dislodged must be replaced. It is necessary to ensure that operatives are adequately protected and the potential environmental hazards such as dust, spent abrasive, and abrasive-laden run-off are dealt with properly.

Rust converters

Rust converters are liquids which, when applied to unstable iron corrosion products, convert them into stable compounds. They can be particularly useful when applied to a complex joint which is heavily corroded and unable to be released to enable complete removal of rust. Three categories of rust-converting products are available:[2]

1. Orthophosphoric acid-based rust converters convert iron oxides into iron phosphates, grey-coloured stable corrosion products.
2. Tannic acid-based converters convert iron oxides and other corrosion products into complex organo-metallic compounds which include iron tannates which are blue-black in colour.

    The first type of tannic acid-based converter contains the acid, a small amount of orthophosphoric acid and a wetting agent with an organic solvent. These products can be applied repeatedly to rust which is untreated or newly appeared.

    The second type includes the same ingredients as well as a synthetic resin in suspension. The resin of the coating can prevent subsequent retreatments from being fully effective.

    Care must be taken in the use of tannic acid-based converters adjacent to masonry. These can cause semi-permanent stain of masonry by converting ferric and ferrous oxides within the surface into tannates.

3. Silicate-based corrosion inhibitors which lead to the formation of the stable compounds goethite and magnetite and which reinstate the alkali conditions necessary for the continued stability and corrosion resistance of steel in concrete.

All three rust conversion systems can be followed by a standard paint system.

Re-rusting of cleaned surfaces

Cast iron or wrought iron members which have been cleaned by flame or dry abrasive should be primed before rust starts to form. If this is not possible then the surface should be flash cleaned immediately prior to priming.

After wet abrasive cleaning, an iron surface will re-rust quite quickly. Also, the surface may remain wet. It is possible to include a rust inhibitor in the final wash and hence delay the need to prime for up to twenty-four hours. The amount of inhibition must be carefully controlled (usually not greater than 5000 ppm) because the excess can cause the deposition of salts which will in turn cause the paint to peel. The water with inhibitor must be carefully removed from horizontal surfaces and water traps. The use of an inhibitor should be agreed with the manufacturer of the selected paint system.

The importance of good site supervision

Proper site supervision by competent staff is important at all stages of work on an historical iron structure but in particular during the preparation for and application of paint. Test areas on all types of surface present, e.g. bars and leafwork, should be observed to ensure the right method or methods of cleaning are chosen. The details of each method should also be resolved at this stage.

5.2 CLEANING OUTDOOR BRONZE SCULPTURE*

Methods for cleaning masonry plinths, etc. should not be applied to bronze sculpture or plaques attached to them. The conservation of a bronze sculpture in an outdoor situation requires detailed understanding of both the object and the corrosion phenomena which are affecting it. A bronze sculpture is a highly complex fabrication which must be treated sensitively. The cleaning of most bronze objects should be undertaken by metals' conservators.

Traditionally, bronze used for statuary is an alloy of about 90 per cent copper and 10 per cent tin, although zinc, aluminium, lead and silver may also be present in very small quantities. It is the best known and most widely used alloy of copper. Bronze is a salmon-gold coloured metal which is seldom seen without the dark brown-red of the patinated or oxidized surface or the green and black corrosion patina which develop in urban, marine or industrial atmospheres. In the latter part of the nineteenth century, colouration was achieved by several means including treatment with heat and/or chemicals and the surface application of pigment.[3]

Prime corrosive agents

The three prime corrosive agents – moisture, gaseous sulphur and nitrogen compounds, and particulate matter – work with other gaseous pollutants and oxygen to corrode the surfaces of unprotected bronze. The atmospheric agents work on the basis of a combination of chemical and electrochemical reactions.

Table 5.1 indicates in simplistic form the commoner active agents and the colour and nature of the salts which are found when they attack bronze in the presence of moisture.

Particulate matter may be inert particles of dirt and dust or it may be particles which contain acidic, bituminous or other corrosive substances. The particles are deposited in dry form as dust or they arrive suspended in rainwater. Particulate matter can act as a catalyst to corrosion and it is desirable to remove it so that electrical corrosion cells are not set up. This is one of the reasons that wax coatings on bronze to which particles adhere readily need to be removed and replaced frequently.

* The material in this section was first published in *Practical Building Conservation: English Heritage Technical Handbook*, Volume 4, *Metals* by Nicola Ashurst and John Ashurst (Aldershot: Gower Technical Press, 1988).

Table 5.1 The effect of corrosive agents on bronze.[4]

Active agent	Salt formed	Colour
Oxygen	Oxide	Red-brown to dark brown and black
Oxygen and chlorine	Chloride or oxychloride	Very pale green
Carbonic acid	Carbonate (malachite)	Green
	Carbonate (azurite)	Blue
Sulphuric acid	Sulphate	Deep blue
	Basic sulphate	Green
Nitric acid	Nitrate (soluble and deliquescent)	Blue-green to blue
Sulphur	Sulphide	Dark brown or black

In an urban, polluted environment or a coastal environment, corrosion will proceed far more rapidly than in an inland rural environment, where the potency, quantity and nature of the corrosive agents is less damaging. Indeed, it is believed that bronze surfaces in urban environments are corroding faster now than in previous decades, due to the increase of oxidizing gases in vehicle emissions.

In a highly polluted, urban environment, surface corrosion may appear rapidly in the form of deep, localized pitting and bright green and black corrosion products. Localized electrochemical corrosion cells usually develop next. Areas covered with dark corrosion products act as cathodes (protected) and those covered with bright green corrosion products act as anodes, under which the most serious loss of metal occurs. The black areas stand proud of the green. During the formation of both the green and the black corrosion layers, the original patina and the surface of the metal are destroyed. If the corrosion process is allowed to continue, disfigurement will result.

The shape of a statue will strongly influence its weathering pattern. Water which collects in crevices will become increasingly corrosive as it evaporates. Unwashed areas are more likely to show serious build-ups of corrosion products than regularly washed convex areas. Unsightly streaks and stains may be the effect of rain on deposits of dust, soot and tar. The degree of corrosive attack of bronze relates directly to the length of time it remains wet or moist, which again relates to shape.

Two other forms of bronze deterioration, which are unlikely to be experienced often in outdoor bronze, are bronze disease and dezincification. Bronze disease most commonly affects bronze artefacts that were buried. It can be a problem where chloride-based de-icing salts are used.

Figure 5.5 Bronze is highly resistant to corrosion in unpolluted environments. Many damaging effects are caused by urban pollution and acid precipitation. Where surface patina and corrosion products are patchy, localized electrochemical corrosion will take place, as is the case here where black surface patches which act as cathodes are intermingled with areas of green corrosion products such as copper sulphate which act as anodes. The purpose of bronze cleaning is to stabilize the metal surface, reducing on-going corrosion as much as possible, and to reinstate the artistic integrity which is so often marred by visually distracting acid precipitation runs, as seen on the side of this urn. This does not require complete removal of all corrosion products, exposing bare metal. Extensive damage has been done to architectural and statuary bronze as the result of misguided and incorrect use of abrasive and chemical cleaning processes. Bronze surfaces may appear robust but in reality are easily damaged. Experience has shown that treatment of their surfaces requires the training and experience of a metals' conservator.

Dezincification is a type of corrosion peculiar to bronze or brass with a composition of more than 15 per cent zinc. It occurs in the presence of acids and other strongly conducting solutions. The copper–zinc alloy is dissolved, the copper is redeposited electrochemically and either the zinc remains in solution or its compounds form a scale. The metal may be left pitted, porous or even weathered, depending on the severity of the dezincification.

The value of patina

The patina or surface colour of bronze determines its appearance and reflects its age and artistic value. The chemical composition of patina is determined by the composition of the metal and the influence of either chemicals applied by man or reagents in the atmosphere, or both. Sometimes the original surface will have been a painted finish, which may not strictly be termed 'patina'.

In an environment without pollution, untreated bronze develops a protective layer of cuprous oxide which is dark brown in colour. Modern air nearly always contains other agents which create other corrosion products of various colours. Basic copper carbonates form a blue-green layer which is unstable in normal environments today. Copper chlorides, also blue and green, are a destructive and undesirable corrosion product. Sulphuric acid agents will produce a pale green patina, and hydrogen sulphide creates a black corrosion product. The history of artificial patination on sculpture and objects of artistic value is over two thousand years old. From the nineteenth century onwards the artificial patination of bronze into colours such as rich chestnut brown, dark brown, black and many shades of green and blue was developed and subsequently practised on a large scale. Applied patina may be excluded by or contained within corrosion products created in the atmosphere.

The issue of the removal or retention of patina is frequently debated in conservation circles. It involves identification of the original patina and subsequent changes to this, and a judgement on whether the corrosion products are disfiguring or destructive. Each situation needs to be judged on its own merits. The necessary investigations, assessment and decisions are the realm of the metals' conservator.

Investigation of bronze statues

The conservation of a bronze artefact in an outdoor exposure requires analysis of the condition of the piece and the corrosion processes before appropriate conservation proposals can be made. It is important to recognize the difference of approach between architectural bronze elements and bronze sculpture.

The inspection, assessment and remedial work on a bronze sculpture should be undertaken only by a metals' conservator. The Museums and Galleries Commission of London and the Metals Section of the Institute for Conservation (UKIC) have both established lists of metal sculpture conservators who can be consulted and commissioned. Irreparable damage can easily be done by those who are insufficiently trained.

The cleaning of bronze may simply involve the removal and re-placement of a protective coating. At the more severe end of the scale, it may involve the removal of corrosion products and patina, repatination and the application of protective coatings. Where architectural bronzes are involved, cleaning should always be undertaken by an experienced metal sculpture conservator who will have the necessary awareness of the art-historical value of the piece and the skills to initiate analytical investigations required to identify all corrosion products present and to determine whether these are damaging and in need of removal.

Making the decision to clean

Before the decision is made to clean a bronze sculpture or a cleaning treatment selected, the following questions need to be answered:

1. What will the cleaning accomplish? Why is it necessary?
2. What was the original designer's or manufacturer's intent?
3. Can the corrosion be removed without too much harm and what will be left if it is removed?
4. Why is the object being cleaned, how much damage is acceptable and what is the acceptable level of clean?
5. What will it look like after it is cleaned?
6. What limitations does the object impose on the cleaning?
7. How big is it, can it be removed or dismantled, what materials are involved?
8. How severe is the corrosion?

9. What is causing the corrosion and can it be eliminated or reduced?
10. How severe is the damage?
11. What are the corrosion products and are they loosely or firmly attached?
12. How will the cleaning affect the object's future performance?
13. Will a protective coating need to be applied?
14. What are the maintenance obligations and when should it be recleaned?

The removal of grease and dirt

This section considers the removal of dirt and grease from bronze as part of a maintenance programme. The removal of corrosion products is considered in the following section.

Dirt on bronze is usually composed of particles of dirt in a binding medium of oil or grease. The particles can contain corrosive acids which will gradually pit the surface of the metal beneath and cause staining. Even if the particles are chemically neutral, they can initiate an electrochemical cell. The dirt can be easily removed and will do little damage if it is frequently removed as part of a maintenance programme.

In such situations cleaning can be achieved by washing with a non-ionic soap in warm water, using a lint-free cloth or natural bristle brush (copper, brass, bronze or ferrous brushes should not be used). Washing should be followed by thorough rinsing, drying with another cloth and the immediate application of a thin protective coating. The soap may need to be diluted in equal parts with water or white spirit to remove greasy dirt. This simple method will not affect insoluble corrosion products or patina. Glass fibre brushes and wooden scrapers can be used to remove loosely adherent material such as bird droppings. Any protective coating would need to be repaired in such areas. In any cleaning operation, small, natural bristle brushes are recommended as these will give controlled and gentle scrubbing.

Where it is necessary to clean and degrease only superficially, all acid- and alkali-based solutions should be avoided as well as all abrasive agents. The same applies to the traditional use of ammonia solutions, which can remove patina and form an orange coloured surface. The solvent trichloroethane is a successful degreaser but it is highly toxic. A better approach is a non-caustic degreasing gel, several of which are readily available.

Should it be necessary to remove paint from bronze, a non-caustic paint remover is preferable. Acetone can usually remove marker pen successfully.

Pigeon droppings contain a high proportion of soluble salts. A layer of droppings produces a corrosive poultice beneath which severe corrosion will occur if it is not removed quickly. Water which runs off collections of droppings can produce very disfiguring streaking.

Degreasing should involve thorough washing and drying if it occurs after washing and before the application of a protective coating. If the water used during the washing or degreasing of bronze is hard, it is advisable to use distilled or deionized water in the final wash. It is always advisable to dry bronze after a period of wetting to avoid water spotting. During this and any other method of cleaning, ladders, sheeting, scaffold poles and ropes must not be allowed to come into contact with the bronze for periods of more than a day. Corrosion can easily be set up at points of contact, causing the loss of patina at least.

Removal of surface layers of corrosion products

The corrosion products on a bronze sculpture may need to be re-moved, for one of several reasons. The products themselves may be promoting further corrosion, they may be marring the aesthetic appearance of the bronze (spotting or streaking), or they may form a non-adherent layer which would provide an unsound basis for a protective coating.

Air abrasive techniques

During the 1980s small-scale air abrasive methods have been used for the cleaning of outdoor bronze sculpture. One of the best known methods is micro-blasting with smooth glass beads (75–125 microns) through an air abrasive pencil or a light duty suction gun at 80–100 psi (11–14 kPa). The surface of the bronze may be reworked or 'peened' by this method and it is now viewed with less favour as a result. Alternative air-driven abrasives which have a gentler action include crushed walnut shells, corn husks and coconut shells. These also have the potential for physically altering the bronze surface and have been known to leave more tenacious corrosion products behind.

Air abrasive methods can be used selectively to reduce thicknesses of localized areas of encrusted soiling prior to a second phase of cleaning of

Figure 5.6 Success in the cleaning of corroded bronze has been achieved in the USA using crushed walnut shell abrasive. Used by trained operatives in the maintenance programme of exterior bronzes of cities such as Washington, the abrasive is applied at air pressures of 20–30 psi (3–4.5 kPa). The stream is directed at 70 degrees to the surface and used at working distances of 50–120 mm (2–8 in.). In this photograph, the small scale pot which is used is being filled with crushed walnut shell abrasive.

the complete surface. The skill of the operator and the choice of powder are critical. Particularly promising results have been achieved using aluminium oxide abrasive which some believe to be less damaging than chemicals, including EDTA. Larger-scale abrasive cleaning machines, higher pressures or more cutting abrasives should never be used.

Chemical compounds

Chelating agents are chemical compounds which interact with select metal ions of corrosion products. They surround the ion, converting it to a soluble complex which can then be rinsed from the metal surface. Chelating agents which have an affinity for the corrosion ions to hand need to be used at the appropriate strength and pH. Four chelating agents that have an affinity for copper are EDTA, glycine, glutamic acid and ammonium citrate. Because of its fast action, EDTA can be effective in breaking down thick layers of corrosion but works too fast and in a manner which is not fully controllable on thin corrosion.[5] The selected agents need to be combined into a solution which is stable, and localized testing and evaluation is essential. This work is definitely the realm of metals' conservators.

Polishing liquids

While chemical cleaning agents remove corrosion products by dissolving them, mechanical methods remove them by physical impact. Polishing liquids include both chemical cleaning agents and fine abrasive. They clean predominantly by abrasion, i.e. removal of metal surface. Although they are readily available they are best not used on any surface of art-historical value.

Electrolytic reduction

Electrolytic reduction is often limited to small artefacts. These are placed in a solution which carries an electric current and the corrosion products are converted back into the base metal. It is also possible to use the method locally on larger items which are not immersed. Its use is usually restricted to the museum field.

Figure 5.7 The surfaces of cleaned bronzes are treated with combinations of carnauba (Brazil) wax and artificial waxes, the corrosion-inhibiting lacquer Incralac or both, to restrict contact between the bronze and its corrosion-inducing environment. Most waxes require removal and reapplication on an annual basis. Lacquer coatings also require maintenance and replacement, although at less frequent intervals (one year in heavily polluted environments and up to four years in cleaner environments). Frequent maintenance is the key to the well-being of all exterior bronzes.

Selecting a method of cleaning

It is not possible to recommend one particular cleaning system, mechanical or chemical, which is the more appropriate in all situations. Any particular piece of bronze that needs cleaning will have its own requirements, limitations and possibilities. These must first be understood and must form the basis for the selection of a cleaning system or combination of cleaning systems.

If cleaning is undertaken in situ, pedestals, plinths and paving should be protected from all cleaning processes with plastic sheet and tape on battens pinned into masonry joints with non-ferrous or galvanized nails.

Protection following cleaning

Surface coatings such as wax, lanolin and lacquer provide a barrier which prevents the corrosive impurities of the atmosphere coming into direct contact with bronze. Once a bronze surface has been cleaned and active corrosion products removed, surface coating is still the best approach to the conservation of bronze surfaces.

Today, the surface coatings include lanolin, traditional natural waxes, synthetic waxes and acrylic lacquers. At times the corrosion inhibitor Benzotriazole is added to these. While some coatings may last slightly longer than others, all should be considered as preventive maintenance treatments which require repair or renewal to remain effective. Paints are generally not an appropriate approach to bronze protection from an aesthetic or a technical point of view. Those which are water porous or which craze can encourage corrosion to be initiated beneath them.

5.3 CLEANING DECORATIVE LEADWORK*

Lead is the softest of the common metals and in a refined form is very malleable. It is capable of being shaped with ease at ambient temperatures without the need for periodic softening or annealing, since

---

* This section includes information first published in *Practical Building Conservation: English Heritage Technical Handbook*, Volume 4, *Metals*, Chapters 5 and 8 by Nicola Ashurst and John Ashurst (Aldershot: Gower Technical Press, 1988). Details on the conservation and repair of lead sheet roofing and repair of lead sheet roofing and lead sculpture can be found in this reference, Chapters 5 and 6.

it does not appreciably work-harden. Lead sheet can, therefore, be readily manipulated with hand-tools without the risk of fracture. It can also be readily manipulated by the technique of bossing.

The main use of lead in historic buildings was in comparatively thick sheets as a roof covering, accompanied by lead gutters, flashings, downpipes and rainwater heads. It is also used to make lead cames, the H- and C-section strips which are soldered to form a substantial part of the support structure for the various glass shapes of 'leaded light' windows.

Lead has been employed ornamentally in the form of church fonts and figures, urns and fountains for gardens, civic squares and stately homes. The cleaning, repair, maintenance and conservation of these works of art require a special balance between the skills of the plumber/craftsman and the sculptor/artist and therefore remains in the realm of the metals' conservator.

Weathering of external leadwork

Lead is extremely resistant to corrosion by the atmosphere, whether in urban, country or coastal areas. In time, lead develops a strongly adhering and highly insoluble patina of lead sulphate, which is silver grey in colour. Lead weathers in two stages. In the first stages of exposure it forms a surface film of lead carbonate* which imparts a light grey appearance, is only loosely adherent to the lead and can wash off. Eventually the permanent patina of lead sulphate develops as a result of reaction with carbon dioxide and, more importantly, with sulphur dioxide in the atmosphere to give an even coloured and adherent patina. The underside of lead sheet which is not exposed to the atmosphere does not develop this protective patina of lead sulphate and hence is susceptible to condensation corrosion.

Cleaning lead

It is rare that lead roofs need to be cleaned. However, they should be kept clear of corrosive pigeon droppings. Dirt on exposed lead should be

---

* Lead carbonate is a toxic dust. Operatives and nearby personnel must be protected from it while it remains in contact with the lead surface or when it becomes airborne. Condensation corrosion includes significant amounts of lead carbonate (lead oxide and lead hydroxide are also present). Its removal requires vacuuming with equipment suited for toxic dust removal. The operation must be carefully controlled from the point of view of health and safety.

Figure 5.8 Conservation of the eighteenth-century lead sculpture of 'Charity' included paint analysis to determine the original colour scheme, followed by removal of corrosion products and a recent bitumastic paint using gels. Further works included lead repairs and the installation of an internal armature. All aspects required the special skills of conservators at the Ornamental Smiths Workshop of English Heritage. (English Heritage)

removed with a non-ionic soap in warm water applied with a bristle brush. Basic lead carbonate can be removed with a number of EDTA-based products. The pH of these solutions must be carefully controlled. Microblasting with glass beads or coconut shells has severe health and safety implications and will rework the lead in a manner which can affect the integrity of surfaces of art-historical value.

Removal of paint from lead should be undertaken by chemical means, preferably using a solvent-based stripper which does not introduce chlorides as these can induce corrosion. (See also Chapter 7, Volume 2, for further discussion regarding the use of solvent-based paint removers.) Rinse-water pressures must be kept low and applied sensibly.

Ultra-high pressure water at 15,000–30,000 psi emanating from an oscillating sapphire head is reported to have been used successfully in the USA to remove lead corrosion products with no mechanical effect on the lead surface. This method will certainly be worthy of consideration should it become generally available here.

5.4 REMOVING PAINT FROM TIMBER

The recommendations in this section may be considered cautious because of the characteristics of timber, and because the removal of thick layers of hardened paint from soft timber substrates does require an extremely cautious approach. It should be remembered that where moderately thick layers are to be removed, the majority of situations will mean dealing with lead-based paint, its removal and disposal of residues.

Paint on exterior timber was intended to be a temporary physical shield primarily from humidity. Throughout the process of weathering, paint layers gradually deteriorate. Depending on the degree of deterioration, selective removal or complete removal may be required. Removal of some kind is frequently required as the life of new paint-work depends on the soundness of the substrate beneath. It is not always necessary to remove paint completely to provide such a sound substrate.

The main role of paint on interior timber surfaces was a decorative one. Internal paintwork may be very thick, reflecting the number of times internal decorations have been changed. It will not have been ravaged by external weather conditions. Grounds for removal are more likely to be excessive thickness hiding detail and poor intercoat adhesion due to poor surface preparation or incompatibility between paint types used. The removal of paint from these surfaces is complicated by difficulties in controlling water run-off and in providing sufficient ventilation.

Paint removal from all timber surfaces is usually a difficult and time-consuming process. Special materials, equipment and expertise are required, not only to remove the paint but to deal with the inherent health and safety dangers and the many associated protection works.

Before work begins, it is essential to check that the painted surfaces are indeed timber and that the timber section beneath the paint has not deteriorated to such an extent that replacement is required. Where appropriate, archaeological approval for the work should be obtained.

Range of external conditions: degree of paint removal[6]

No paint removal is required when the following conditions are present:

1. Environmental soiling or organic matter such as surface dirt, soot, pollution, cobwebs, and insect cocoons which cling to the painted surface and can be a barrier to proper adhesion of a subsequent paint coat can be rinsed from the paint surface with a solution of detergent and water applied with a soft, bristle brush, rinsed thoroughly with clean water.
2. Mildew will thrive in areas of dampness and lack of sunshine. The fungal growths feed on nutrients in the paint and on dirt adhering to its surface. Mildew can be removed using a solution of non-ammoniated detergent, household bleach and water (in equal parts) applied and scrubbed in with a soft bristle brush and then rinsed.
3. Chalking or powdering of a paint surface is caused by gradual disintegration of the resin in the paint film. The chalk can be removed with a detergent solution and scrubbing with natural bristle brushes.
4. Paint layers which are stained by fixings within the wood or components of the wood itself do not need removal unless the cause of the staining needs to be dealt with.

Limited paint removal will be required from surfaces exhibiting the following conditions:

1. Crazing of paint layers on wood takes place when thick and brittle layers of paint are no longer able to expand and contract with the movement of the timber substrate in its responses to temperature and humidity changes. The situation needs to be corrected to prevent moisture entering through the crazed surface.

2. Inter-coat peeling can be the result of improper cleaning or preparation of painted surfaces prior to repainting. Another cause of inter-coat failure is incompatibility between paint types, for example oil paint and latex paint. In both situations the paint needs to be removed by manual scraping and sanding to beyond the layer of inter-coat failure but no further if all other layers are well adhered.

3. Solvent blistering of a paint surface takes place when the surface of a layer which is applied dries too quickly and its solvents are trapped. The solvent eventually vaporizes and forces its way through the paint surface by forming blisters. Blistering can be caused by moisture, and the cutting open of blisters to reveal their contents and the substrate beneath will indicate whether solvent or moisture is the cause. Solvent blisters are generally smaller than moisture blisters. It is necessary only to remove the blistered surface before re-painting.

4. Wrinkling of a paint surface occurs when the top of a paint film dries before the underneath. The whole wrinkled layer and often the layer immediately below should be removed by scraping and sanding.

In many instances the condition of paint will be such that total removal is required to provide a sound substrate for repainting. If this is the case, the chronology of historical paint layers should be investigated and recorded and, if possible, an inconspicuous area of the full complement of decorations be left as a physical record of the building's paint history.

Paint surface conditions which normally demand *total paint removal* are:

1. Peeling to bare timber. This is usually caused by the entry of excessive amounts of moisture into the timber. The first step must be to locate and remove the source or sources of the moisture. Once the timber has been left to dry out thoroughly, damaged paint can be removed by manual scraping and manual or mechanical sanding.

2. Cracking or crocodiling (alligatoring). These are advanced stages of crazing and are caused by moisture penetration of less serious defects until the paint is cracked through to the wood. The cracking eventually takes on a pattern of horizontal and vertical lines which make it look like the skin of a reptile. Only the layers affected by cracking need to be removed.

Paint removal methods

The removal of paint from timber must take into consideration the following issues:

1. The health and safety of the individuals undertaking the work.
2. The continued protection, preservation or decoration of the historic timber.
3. The retention of the sequence of historic paint layers.

Mechanical methods

Areas of paint which have been affected by crazing, inter-coat peeling, blistering or wrinkling can often be dealt with by manual scraping and either manual or mechanical sanding. Putty knives and paint scrapers used in removing the affected layer or layers must be used with care to avoid gouging the wood beneath. The resultant surface can be smoothed or feathered by sanding using paper supported by wood, rubber blocks or a sponge where feathering needs to extend into grooves and other irregular surfaces. All sanding should be done along the grain.

Large flat areas which have been scraped can be sanded by mechanical means. Orbital sanders are effective in feathering scraped areas and in removing limited numbers of paint layers. They are more controllable than belt sanders and have less potential for damage to the paint or the wood. Rotary drill attachments such as sanding discs and wire brushes should be avoided as they can easily leave visible circular depressions or shred the wood surface.

Medium to high pressure water should also be avoided because of the amounts of water it can force into the wood grain.

While wet and dry abrasive cleaning will be effective in removing paint, they frequently scar the wooden surfaces beneath. The processes cannot differentiate between the softer fibres of the spring wood and the harder, denser fibres of the summer wood, and often result in a pitted surface with ridges and valleys. As with masonry, abrasive cleaning can also damage projecting areas of carvings and mouldings before paint from concave areas is removed. In the context of removal of paint from exterior woodwork, abrasive cleaning methods are potentially one of the most damaging.

All the abrasive methods listed above, both manual and mechanical, must take into consideration the health and safety issues of dealing with lead dust, eye damage and disposal of lead paint residue.

Thermal methods

Thermal methods are normally used on surfaces where total paint removal is necessary. Until recently, blow torches and hot air blowers were used to soften and blister paint, enabling it to be scraped from the surface. Today, because of awareness of the fire hazards associated with the use of open flames, it is unlikely that the use of a blow torch will be accepted on an historic buildings site in the UK. Hot air blowers are also being viewed with suspicion because of their potential for establishing fire hazards.

The flames of propane and/or butane torches bubble and loosen paint enabling it to be scraped off but they are also capable of scorching and igniting the wood, burning the operator and causing him severe injury to eyes and skin. Flames at high temperatures vaporize lead-based paints, releasing toxic fumes which may be inhaled.

Hot air blowers (heat guns) produce streams of hot air which are directed against the painted woodwork to soften and lift the paint. Equipment which produces air at temperatures up to 190°C (400°F) is preferred. Much greater care is needed in the use of blowers which operate at 350°C (600°F) and 500°C (930°F). The guns work best on heavy paint build-ups and are particularly effective for removing paint from within detailed work. A considerable amount of skill is required to ensure that paint is softened only as much as necessary and before charring of extremities of decorative areas takes place. Hot air blowers may also create heat build-ups within recesses.

Both thermal methods require precautions against fire, lead fumes, eye damage and burning of the operative, as well as disposal of the lead paint residue.

Figure 5.9 Cleaning trials on this panelled timber door were undertaken with solvent strippers of gel and poultice consistency. The best result was achieved when the bulk of layers was first removed using hot air. The door could be moved into the open air for this to be undertaken safely. Slight charring of surfaces could have been caused by incorrect use of the hot air blower. The two test areas on which this equipment had not been used confirmed a previous paint removal operation as the source of the charring.

Chemical methods

Solvent-based and alkaline-based strippers play a rather supplementary role on timberwork, principally because their removal involves the use of water. They are nevertheless effective in softening paint residue in intricate, decorative features and in cracks or other areas which are hard to reach by hot air blowers. They are particularly useful on window mullions where heat-producing devices could easily break the glass.

Until the development of solvent-based strippers, alkaline-based strippers were used exclusively for chemical removal of paint. The potential for deposition of soluble salt residues in timber surfaces is as great a problem as it is with masonry. Fortunately, commercial dip stripping companies have transferred from caustic baths to baths of different formulations. The wood left in caustic baths was adversely affected by both the alkaline stripper and the water. Even in localized applications, alkaline strippers deplete timber and lift its grain. Their use is frequently avoided for this reason.

All chemical paint removers are deemed hazards under health and safety requirements. The cost of minimizing the risk of their use should not be overlooked.

The formulas of solvent-based strippers tend to vary, 'but generally consist of combinations of organic solvents such as methylene chloride, isopropanol, toluol, xylol, and methanol; thickeners such as methyl cellulose; and various additives such as paraffin wax used to prevent the volatile solvents from evaporating before they have time to soak through multiple layers of paint.'[7] Some are more thixotropic than others making them more suited for use on vertical surfaces. From a health and safety point of view, 'the vapors from the organic chemicals can be highly toxic if inhaled; skin contact is equally dangerous because the solvents can be absorbed; . . . many solvent-based strippers are flammable.'[8]

In the USA the use of methylene chloride-based strippers is being controlled to an increasing extent, and the ban which is in force in California is expected to be applied elsewhere. It is possible that their use will eventually be similarly controlled in the UK. Several environmentally friendly products in alternative solvents are already available, although most do not act as swiftly as the methylene chloride-based products. It will be necessary to adapt paint removal operations to suit their particular manner of working. Experience in their usage is not widespread at this stage.

Solvent-based strippers which are water rinsable can create much mess if the rinsing off of dissolved paint and remaining stripper is not undertaken in a very careful and controlled manner, including protection of associated surfaces. Water-rinsable stripper will tend to raise the grain of the wood more than white spirit-based strippers.

Proprietary paint removal packs are widely used on timber for the removal of thick layers of paint because they enable use of limited quantities of water. Thick layers of sticky paste, either solvent- or alkaline-based are applied and covered for dwell times of around twenty-four hours. Generally, the softened paint is lifted from the surface as the cover sheeting is removed. Limited scraping can be necessary and controlled rinsing must follow. With these products it is possible to collect most of the softened paint and pack it for safe disposal. For further discussion of paint removal poultices, see Chapter 7, Volume 2.

Health and safety considerations relating to the use of chemical strippers include taking precautions against inhaling toxic vapours, fire, eye damage and chemical poisoning from skin contact. Disposal of residues of lead-based paints in accordance with environmental legislation must be considered an essential part of the stripping operation. Sludge of lead-based paint which is scraped off, rather than rinsed off, can be disposed of by collection in a tin which has a wire stretched across the top which the scraping knife is run across to deposit the sludge into the can. When the can is full, the wire can be removed, the lid put on the can and the residue disposed of according to local authority regulations.[9]

REFERENCES

1. References are listed in: Ashurst, J. and N. (1988) *Practical Building Conservation: English Heritage Technical Handbook*, Volume 4, *Metals*. Aldershot: Gower Technical Press.
2. Weaver, M.E. with Matero, F.G. (1993), *Conserving Buildings: A Guide to Techniques and Materials*. New York: John Wiley, p.187.
3. La Niece, S. and Craddock, P. (1993) *Metal Plating & Patination. Cultural, technical & historical developments*. Oxford: Butterworth/Heinemann.
4. Jack, J.F.S. (1951) The cleaning and preservation of bronze statues, *The Museums Journal*, Vol. 50, No. 10, January, p.231.
5. Heuman, J. (1992) Removing corrosion on a painted outdoor bronze sculpture with mild chelating agents, *The Conservator*, 16, pp.12–17.
6. Weeks, K.D. and Look, D.W. (1982) *Exterior Paint Problems on Historic Woodwork: Preservation Briefs 10*, Technical Preservation Services Division, Heritage Conservation and Recreation Service, Washington: US Government Printing Office.
7. Ibid., p.11.
8. Ibid., p.11.
9. Ibid., p.11.

Chapter Six

Case Studies

Except for Case Study 1, Cleopatra's Needle, the case studies in this chapter involve projects undertaken by the author in her capacity as manager of Adriel Consultancy in Nottingham, a consultancy which provides analytical, diagnostic and specification skills to the building conservation industry in the UK. These projects involved detailed surveying and analysis of historic facades and the undertaking of on-site trials prior to specification preparation. One involved a programme of analysis integrated with the cleaning and surface repair assessments. In the remaining studies, analysis was undertaken as was appropriate and possible within the practical and financial limits of each situation. Not unexpectedly, situations were not always ideal, some being closer to perfect than others. Readers are encouraged to learn from these experiences, to appreciate what was done, as well as the many problems that were avoided as a result of the detailed processes of assessment, analysis and specification that were undertaken. Further issues and details are discussed in the second set of case studies at the end of Volume 2.

6.1 CASE STUDY 1: CLEOPATRA'S NEEDLE, THE EMBANKMENT, LONDON – CHRONOLOGY OF SURFACE TREATMENTS UP TO THE 1950s

Introduction

The monolithic piece of pinkish Egyptian granite of the shaft of Cleopatra's Needle has a well-recorded history of nearly three-and-a-half thousand years. It has been in its present location on the Thames River embankment since 1878. In 1993, the surfaces of the granite are slightly soiled and the granite is flaking off in pieces of up to one inch in length.

This case study presents the text of an article dating from 1952 by acknowledged stone experts of that time, S.G. Burgess, Deputy Chief Chemist of London County Council and R.J. Schaffer, DSIR, Building Research Station, Garston, Hertfordshire. It records their observations of the granite surfaces and the information collected regarding previous cleaning and surface treatment operations. It is a valuable historical record of expert attitudes to the condition and cleaning of the masonry surface of a national monument many would be hesitant to touch today without the benefit of research and analysis to establish the exact causes of the granite's decay. Records of works undertaken since that time are on the files of the former Greater London Council (GLC). Following its demise, responsibility for Cleopatra's Needle transferred from the GLC via the London Division of English Heritage to Westminster City Council.

The Burgess and Schaffer article shows that between arrival in London in 1878 and 1952 the surfaces of the Needle had been the subject of numerous interventions which by current conservation understanding would be considered drastic. These works alone present a very strong case for the need for petrographic and chemical analysis to establish the effect of the treatments, the extent of soluble salt crystallization and the role of the constituents of the granite in its breakdown prior to any further intervention. (See also Erhard Winkler's article 'Historical implications of destructive salt weathering – Cleopatra's Needle, New York', *APT Bulletin* XII, No.2, 1980, p.84.)

The modes of deterioration recorded in the Burgess and Schaffer article are observable today. In most areas, the granite surface is rough and fissured. The granite continues to experience surface spalling with lens-shaped losses of up to 2 in. across and 0.25 in. thick. Fragments continue to be removable by fingernail with soiling and algal growths being found behind many of these. There is a dull greyish hue to the granite surface which may be attributable to coating residues and the effects of chemical cleaning.

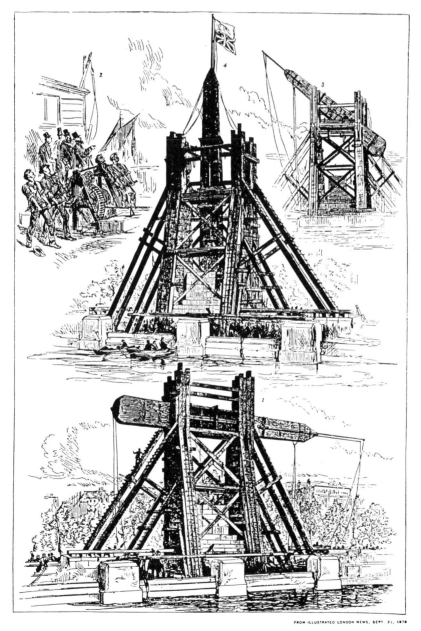

FROM ILLUSTRATED LONDON NEWS, SEPT. 21, 1878

Figure 6.1 Cleopatra's Needle, the London obelisk, in process of erection on the north bank of the Thames in 1878.

Figure 6.2 Surface condition and weathering patterns of the granite of Cleopatra's Needle in the upper third zone of the north and west faces, 1992.

Cleopatra's Needle

The following is the text of the article 'Cleopatra's Needle' by S.G. Burgess, BSc., PhD., FRIC and R.J. Schaffer, BSc., MA, published in *Chemistry and Industry* (1952), pp. 1026–1029.

A decision of the London County Council to clean Cleopatra's Needle in the summer of 1949 made it necessary to consider whether a chemical detergent could safely and effectively be used and what steps might afterwards be taken to preserve the stone, so far as may be, from future deterioration. The Council's records of the condition of the stone and of the preservatives that have been applied to it from time to time were consulted and enquiries were made about the similar obelisk in New York. The information collected is put on record here, together with a description of the recent work and of the observations made in the course of it.

Descriptions of Cleopatra's Needle and its history are to be found in the standard works of Erasmus Wilson (1887) and Wallis Budge (1926). Fashioned from a monolith of pinkish granite from the quarries of Suwan (Syene of the Greeks and modern Aswan) on the east bank of the Nile at the foot of the first cataract, it is stated to be 68 ft 5 ½ ins high and to weigh upwards of 186 tons, and is believed to have been first erected at On (Heliopolis) about 1500 BC. Having been presented to the British people in 1819, it was brought from Egypt after the lapse of more than half a century and reached London on January 20, 1878, after an eventful journey, the story of which is well known. It was erected on its present site on September 12, 1878. The Monuments (Metropolis) Act of 1878 placed it in the care of the Metropolitan Board of Works and gave the power to erect in association with it any appropriate works of art. Responsibility passed to the London County Council when that body was formed in 1889.

Records of the condition of the stone and its treatment,
1879–1932

The first reference to the condition of the obelisk after its arrival in Britain is found in a report by Sir J. W. Bazalgette (Chief Engineer to the Metropolitan Board of Works) and Keates (Consulting Chemist) dated July 29, 1879. After making a thorough examination of the stone, they reported that 'it was greatly damaged – not by mechanical means but by very gradual decomposition of the granite.' Exfoliation of the surface was taking place and scales of some thickness could be detached, especially near the base. This damage was considered to be due not to chemical substances abnormally present in the air but rather to the physical action of water and subsequent frost. It was recommended that a preservative solution that would not materially change the appearance of the monument should be applied. After extensive enquiry, 'stone solution' prepared by the Indestructible Paint Company was recommended. The stone was thoroughly cleaned in 1879. The solution, which is reported to have consisted of Dammar resin and wax in petroleum spirit, was then applied to the stone 'until it would not absorb any more'. Considerable anxiety was expressed at that time about the possible effects of exposing the stone to 'the humid atmosphere near the River Thames and to the dirt of the Metropolis.'

A few years later, in a Cantor lecture, Dent (1887) refers to American reports which led him to infer that the effects of the weather on the similar obelisk in New York had been much greater than those experienced in London. He states that the treatment used in London in 1879 was applied in several coats, starting with a very weak solution, and comments that after eight years the treatment appeared to have been of service, but he reserved judgment pending further experience.

In 1890, John Dixon, CE, who had been responsible for transporting the obelisk to London and erecting it, examined the stone and reported that he had failed to detect any sign of decay. Judging from letters to the press, there were still some doubts, despite this assurance; the Home Secretary, Henry Matthews, is reported to have said that the London atmosphere had affected the Needle to a depth of ½ in.

In 1894, W.J. Dibdin (Chief Chemist to the London County Council) and A.R. Binney (Chief Engineer) examined the stone up to a height of 10–15 ft on the NE side and 30 ft on the NW side. They reported that on both sides it was very noticeable that there was more attack at the bottom of the hieroglyphs than at the top of them. On the NE side only a few pieces of the stone could be separated with the fingernail and there was very little sign of disintegration. The NW face, however, was in a much worse condition. The surface was covered with minute fissures and it was an easy matter to separate particles of granite. The action on this face appeared to be more general than on the NE side; the separated pieces were larger and apparently more decayed, being quite easily separable and weathered on both the outer and inner surfaces. It was said that there was also a slight appearance of vegetable growth, described as lichen, and that the stone was decidedly porous, changing in colour and taking up water readily from a wet sponge. It was concluded that the treatment fifteen years previously with Dammar resin and wax in petroleum had been fairly successful, taking into consideration the bad atmospheric conditions in the metropolis. Recommendations were made for the treatment to be repeated in order that the surface of the stone should be 'completely saturated with the protective medium.' This work was carried out in 1895.

In 1910 W.E. Riley (Architect to the London County Council) and Dr F. Clowes (Chief Chemist) made a full report on the condition of the obelisk. They stated that there was no doubt that, although chemical action appeared to be taking place at only a relatively slow rate, the physical action of moisture and frost was of a comparatively serious nature. Fragments could be removed with the fingernail and the partly blackened posterior surfaces of such fragments showed that water and soot had been able to penetrate the fissures.

Figure 6.3 Detail of spalling and soiling to upper levels of the west face of Cleopatra's Needle (1992). The granite surface is visibly fissured in areas of heaviest deterioration. Many granite spalls up to 50 mm (2 in.) in length, such as the one being indicated, are on the verge of becoming detached.

One of the officers who examined the obelisk on this occasion had taken part in the examination made in 1894 and was of the opinion that the condition of the surface was very similar to that observed on the previous occasion. It was recommended that the stone should be cleaned and preservative treatment applied and that 'this should be repeated at intervals of, say, not more than five years.' The report includes a comment to the effect that, 'Having regard to the climatic and atmospheric conditions prevailing in this country and more particularly in large towns we feel that the exposure of valuable stone monuments such as this in the open air is undesirable.' In 1911 the stone was cleaned and then treated by a process which is described as having been used with success elsewhere by Sir Arthur Church, FRS. This consisted in applying with a brush an ointment composed of solid paraffin or ceresin partly dissolved in a suitable vehicle, allowing this to evaporate, and then warming with a spirit lamp or some suitable appliance. The method used for cleaning the stone is not recorded.

No further action was taken until 1932 when the London Fire Brigade washed the stone with water under pressure from a fire appliance. Scaffolding was not erected and there is no report on the condition of the stone.

Enquiries on the condition of Cleopatra's Needle,
New York

Before the work to be described was undertaken, enquiries were made through the UK Scientific Mission in Washington about the condition of the corresponding obelisk, also known as Cleopatra's Needle, which stands in Central Park, New York, about the treatments that had been applied to it.

The obelisk was reported to be in 'quite satisfactory' condition though the granite, in common with other monuments in New York, was said to be subject to a certain amount of spalling. It was treated in 1885 by applying molten paraffin to the warmed granite and subsequentiy reheating the surface to secure better penetration of the wax. The method of heating adopted is not known but it is thought that a metal shield carrying gas-burners was used. Some further work of a similar kind appears to have been done in 1893. In 1914 another treatment, believed to have been a mixture of oils and thinners was applied. There has been much controversy in the United States about whether these treatments have been of value. James Kraus, one of the principals who had been engaged in the work of 1914, reported in 1918 to the firm responsible for the first treatment, saying that he found 'no indication that disintegration was going on' when the new work was undertaken; he stated that comparison with photographs and diagrams of its earlier condition showed that 'no new flakes had developed, neither had any of the original flakes increased in size.' The treatment of the obelisk, he says, 'was allowed to proceed through a misapprehension as to its condition.' In a similar statement in 1933 he confirmed that in his view the treatment applied in 1914 was unnecessary. Dent (1887) implies that there was some unfavourable comment on the original treatment at quite an early stage, but Fink (1934) speaks of it as having been successful and says that 'the ravages of rain and frost that were rapidly obliterating the hieroglyphics on the obelisk have now at least been checked.' Another view is that some of the more obvious damage to the monument had been caused before it left Egypt, and that the treatment applied in 1884 may have appeared to be effective because loose fragments, said by Egleston (1886) to have amounted to at least 800 lb, were removed beforehand. However that may be, reports indicate that the present condition of the stone is regarded as satisfactory. There has at all events been no suggestion that the heating of the granite to secure penetration of the wax has caused harm.

Other enquiries

In response to other enquiries, the Chief Inspector of Ancient Monuments, Ministry of Works, provided information on a method that has been applied on occasion to selected parts of buildings in the care of the Ministry of Works, using wax melted into the surface by the judicious use of a blow-lamp.

Condition of the London obelisk in 1948–9

In August, 1948, temporary scaffolding was erected and the obelisk was inspected to a height of about 20 ft. above its base. A considerable amount of dirt was found adhering to the stone which was generally in a sound state although there were places where small fragments and a few larger flakes up to about 2 in. in diameter could be detached. It was decided by the London County Council that the stone should be cleaned and treated with a preservative. This work began in July, 1949.

The stone was re-examined in 1949 when the whole of the monument had been scaffolded in preparation for cleaning. It was found to be covered for the most part with a hard, black deposit which obscured much of the surface and which subsequently proved exceedingly difficult to remove.

Near the apex and for some distance downwards, all four faces were more or less equally blackened, but towards the base the SW and SE faces were lighter in colour and were so much less obscured that the crystalline texture and pinkish colour of the granite could be seen. The SW face was cleaner than the SE face. Of the NW and NE faces, which were quite black from apex to base, the NW face was slightly the more dirty. Dibdin recorded a similar difference in 1894.

Examination of the surface at the higher levels gave a more favourable impression of the condition of the granite than had been gathered from the preliminary inspection of the lower levels in 1948, for there was practically no sign of flaking other than that which has already been described. On the whole, the amount was quite small in relation to the total area. The tendency to flaking was more noticeable on the dirtier NW and NE faces. Newly-exposed surfaces on these faces were usually found to be dark in colour, whereas the removal of flakes from the SW and SE faces revealed fairly clean surfaces, such as can be seen in the light-coloured patches.

Under the deposited dirt on the NW and NE faces some wax preservative was found, both on the face and more especially in the hieroglyphs. This wax, which was contaminated with tarry matter, was judged from its chemical properties and melting point (139°F) to be the ceresin applied in 1911. It was firmly attached to the stone in 'scales'. Beneath it, the stone was found to be dark in colour, suggesting either that the tarry deposit had penetrated beneath the wax or, more probably, that the cleaning operation of 1911 had not been very successful.

Cleaning in 1949

The black surface deposit was very hard and quite insoluble in water. It could not be removed by ordinary washing methods and assistance was sought in the use of a chemical detergent.

To avoid all possible risk of causing subsequent harm to the granite the detergent to be used was required to be neutral in reaction and free from inorganic salts, especially sulphates. An ethylene oxide condensate (Lissapol N) met these requirements.

By using this detergent in a one per cent solution in water and scrubbing energetically with bristle brushes, the less soiled parts of the SE and SW faces could be cleaned reasonably well. Practically no impression could be made on the other faces even when wire brushes were used. Wire-brushing, which may seem to be a drastic operation, had no effect on the granite except to remove the already loosened flakes, but it was evident that a more effective method would have to be found to facilitate the cleaning and reduce the cost. After experimenting with various solvents, suitably chosen to minimize fire and toxic risks in use, it was found that the tarry deposits could be softened with a mixture consisting of 9 volumes of carbon tetrachloride with 1 volume benzene, emulsified with a 1 per cent solution of the detergent. Though the work was still arduous, this mixture facilitated the cleaning operation and the stone was eventually restored to a reasonably clean state, having a similar colour, a dull pinkish hue, on each face and such that light-coloured patches in places from which flakes had been detached were no longer noticeable. In this state, the form of the in-scriptions could be clearly seen from the ground level, whereas they had previously been almost indistinguishable.

Preservative treatment

Preliminary experiments were undertaken with compounds for sealing the granite surface to prevent the ingress of moisture. Choice was limited, because it was important that the appearance of the stone should not be materially altered. It was eventually decided to use paraffin wax, but instead of one with a high melting point such as was apparently used in 1911, a wax with a lower melting point (120°F) was thought to be preferable. Two applications were given of a 10 per cent solution of this wax in white spirit, and, after allowing the solvent to evaporate, the surface was very gently heated with a blowlamp to melt the wax into the fissures, the aim being to seal these fissures without leaving more than a very thin film of wax on the surface. Examination of the stone after treatment indicated that the object had been achieved and it may be hoped that the ingress of rain and condensed moisture has been materially retarded. Regrettably, however, the stone subsequently darkened in colour and soon lost its freshly-cleaned appearance.

Observations on the surface deposit

The loose flakes collected from the obelisk have been examined in an attempt to determine the nature of the black surface deposit and to find an explanation of how it may have been formed and why it is so hard and intractable. The observations have not led to any firm conclusion but are of sufficient interest to be placed on record.

On some of the flakes the film was continuous and completely masked the surface of the stone. On others, it could be seen under a hand lens to take the form of small, rounded accretions, between which the crystalline surface of the stone could be faintly discerned.

In a thin section under the microscope, the film is seen to have an average thickness of about 0.002 in. It tends to fill depressions in the surface of the stone and to acquire a greater thickness at these points. It is quite opaque and shows no sign of structure or of crystalline inclusions. The break in continuity seen in the illustration [not shown] represents an area from which a smaller flake had been lost before the section was made.

Besides forming this superficial film, black, opaque material fills many of the fissures in the rock, but there are other fissures, appearing in the illustrations [not shown] in a light-grey tint, which can be seen under the microscope to be filled with the coloured synthetic resin used to impregnate the sample to facilitate the preparation of the section. These were open fissures. Most granites are fissured to some extent in the natural state, but it may reasonably be assumed that some of the fissures in the sample have developed by exposure to the weather and that those not filled with the black material are of comparatively recent origin.

The rock itself shows a typical granite texture, with crystals of quartz, plagioclase and orthoclase felspars, hornblende and very small aggregates of white mica. The only accessory mineral in evidence is magnetite, which shows no sign of alteration.

The black film was neither loosened from the stone nor softened to any perceptible extent by prolonged soaking in water. Boiling water, hot hydrochloric acid and warm benzene were all equally ineffective. Hydrofluoric acid had no apparent effect. When the carbonaceous matter was removed by ignition at a dull red heat the colour changed from black to brownish-orange and the deposit then dissolved quite readily in warm hydrochloric acid to give a yellowish solution containing ferric iron.

This solution was evaporated to dryness and examined spectrographically. The spectrograph showed the presence of a high proportion of iron, a surprisingly high proportion of silicon, fairly high magnesium, manganese and calcium, besides potassium, sodium and aluminium. A second treatment of the sample with hydrochloric acid gave no evidence of further extraction of siliceous matter.

An attempt to obtain further information about the character of the film by X-ray analysis was unsuccessful. A sample obtained by careful scraping of one of the flakes, aiming to avoid contamination with mineral matter from the underlying stone, proved to be too small to give any clear pattern.

Judging from the information available, the film seems to consist essentially of carbonaceous matter bound with mineral matter containing silicon and iron as the main elements, but the state of combination of these elements has not been established and it is not known to what extent they originate from the granite itself or from the deposited soot. The iron-bearing minerals in the rock can be seen under the microscope to be fresh and unaltered; hence, soot, which contains a fair proportion of iron, would seem to be the more likely source of iron. Silicon and other elements could be derived from the stone. It may be conjectured that small amounts of silica and other compounds are taken into solution when the stone is wetted by rain and that the redeposition of this matter as the stone dries consolidates the sooty matter trapped on the moist surface, and thus builds up a hard film.

The records give no indication of how thoroughly the stone was cleaned on previous occasions. The observed thickness of the film (ca. 0.002 in.) represents the deposit accumulated over a period of at least 38 years, since the hosing of 1932 would not have affected it. If the absence of any reference in the records to the difficulty of the cleaning operation and the finding of a discoloured surface beneath the surviving traces of wax can be assumed to imply that the existing film was not removed in 1911 or earlier, it represents the accumulation over the whole of the period since the obelisk was erected in London in 1878. Beneath the film, the rock shows its natural texture. There is nothing to suggest that any similar, but cleaner, film was formed over the centuries by exposure to the drier climate of Egypt.

The examination described has exhausted the material available from Cleopatra's Needle. It is to be hoped that opportunity may occur to secure other samples of weathered granite from buildings in London or elsewhere, for comparison of the condition of the surfaces and perhaps to get more precise knowledge of the composition of the superficial deposits.

Acknowledgments

The authors desire to express their thanks to Mr C.J. Regan, BSc., FRIC, Chemist-in-Chief to the London County Council, for his valuable help and criticism, and also to Mr W.B. Gostling, ARIBA, Divisional Architect, LCC, Mr B. St.J. O'Neil, Chief Inspector of Ancient Monuments, Ministry of Works, Mr D.W. Kessler, National Bureau of Standards, Washington, and Mr G.H. Liddle, Department of Commerce, New York, for assistance in collecting the information recorded in this paper.

This account of the work is published by permission of Sir Allen Daley, MD, FRCP., Medical Officer of Health, London County Council; Mr R.H. Matthew, ARIBA, Architect to the London County Council ; and Dr F.M. Lea , CBE, DSc., FRIC, Director of Building Research, Department of Scientific and Industrial Research.

References

Dent, W.Y. (1887). *J. Soc. Arts*, 35, 825, 841, 855, 870.
Egleston, T. (1886). *Trans. Amer. Soc. Civ. Engrs.*, No. 319.
Fink, F.W. (1934). *Chem and Ind.*, 12, 191.
Wallis Budge, A.E. (1926). *Cleopatra's Needles and Other Egyptian Obelisks*, London, Rel. Tract. Soc.
Wilson, E. (1887). *Cleopatra's Needle*, London, Brain & Co.

6.2 CASE STUDY 2: ST MARY'S CHURCH, GATESHEAD – A DETAILED ASSESSMENT OF THE SANDSTONE MASONRY TO DETERMINE THE DESIRABILITY AND FEASIBILITY OF ITS CLEANING

Background and brief

St Mary's Church, Gateshead, is a Grade II* listed building whose chronology of development began in Norman times. Located at the southern end of Tyne Bridge, the church is a prominent landmark to the Newcastle and Gateshead areas. The heavy soiling to many areas of its stone had given the church the name of 'The Black Church'.

In December, 1990, during the early phases of on-site preparations, Adriel Consultancy was commissioned by Architects for the development, K.R. Banyard Ltd, to undertake a detailed study into the desirability and practicalities of cleaning the external masonry of the church. Client for the project was the owner, Phillips Son & Neale Properties. It had been decided that the complexity of the proposed cleaning works needed a thorough specialist study which would investigate and consider the several issues which required evaluation. The specialist investigations were undertaken with the involvement of and on the basis of funding from the Chief Executive's Department of Gateshead Metropolitan Borough Council.

The brief for the consultancy was:

1. To prepare an assessment of the type and general condition of the different types and areas of stonework found in the building.
2. To prepare an assessment of the desirability of undertaking cleaning of the external stonework of St Mary's, with particular reference to the effects of cleaning on the masonry surfaces.

Figure 6.4 Former St Mary's Church, Gateshead, Tyne and Wear, prior to cleaning, repair and refurbishment. The structure was converted into offices, salesrooms and warehousing for Phillips, the antiques auctioneers.

3. To determine whether there were sound technical reasons for *not* cleaning.

4. If stone cleaning was recommended, a full report on the effect of the cleaning, particularly in relation to the resultant colouration of the stonework.

5. To undertake trial panels of selected cleaning methods in locations to be agreed with the client and Gateshead Metropolitan Borough Council on representative areas of masonry type and soiling degree.

6. To prepare a detailed specification for any recommended cleaning methods, including the material(s) to be used, the method of application, dwell time(s), methods of removal, qualifications and supervision of operatives. To include for any directly associated works, for example, pointing.

7. To report in a manner similar to the above on the cleaning of the interior stonework.

8. To consider and report on the repointing of the ashlar masonry of the west tower.

The brief did not require detailed consideration of the remedial works to the stonework which were being dealt with by the architects.

Strategy adopted

The following strategy was adopted.

Investigation and recording on site

The surfaces of the church masonry were inspected as closely as possible with the purpose of noting alterations to the masonry surfaces due to weathering agents, such as water, pollutants, applied coatings and soluble salts, along with the effect of lack of maintenance. Local deterioration problems were noted and assessed within the context of each facade. At this time, samples of stone were taken for use in an analysis programme.

The analysis programme

A scientific analysis programme was undertaken to provide detailed technical information regarding the characteristics of the stone of the church and its modes of decay. A range of petrological, physical and chemical analyses were undertaken to identify the mineralogy of the stone, its chemistry and other essential physical and chemical characteristics. Information provided by the analysis programme included assessment of the potential for damage as the result of the use of chemical cleaning materials and methods. The analysis programme was also designed to investigate whether the masonry already included dangerous levels of pollutants which were an existing major cause of deterioration. The co-ordinating analyst, who had a masonry conservation background, was involved in the taking of all samples.

On-site cleaning trials

A series of on-site cleaning trials of a selected range of cleaning materials and methods was undertaken on representative areas of masonry. These were considered necessary to determine the effectiveness of the selected systems, and to enable more accurate evaluation of the visual implications of undertaking the cleaning of the St Mary's masonry. The trials also proved useful indicators of the constraints which the pre-repair condition of the masonry and associated jointing was to impose on a cleaning programme.

The labour and equipment back-up for the trials was provided by the contractor for the cleaning and remainder of the remedial works programme for St Mary's who had already been engaged. The trials involved a selection of products of the three main chemical cleaning agent suppliers in the UK, as well as dry abrasive and low pressure water systems. Some of the methods were selected by Adriel Consultancy whilst others, due to the advanced stage of the masonry repair contract, were proposed and supplied by the contractor.

Environmental conditions on the days of the trials were not entirely suitable to the use of chemical cleaning agents or the use of water on masonry, as temperatures hovered around 5°C. However, the timescale of this commission did not permit delay of the trials until better weather conditions were assured. The required information was nevertheless obtained from the site cleaning trials, the works being undertaken during the warmest part of the day.

Cleaning assessment and strategy

The findings provided by the inspection of the masonry surfaces, the on-site trials and the results of the analysis programme were evaluated and a strategy for the cleaning prepared.

The preferred and recommended sequence of assessment of masonry, followed by sampling and analysis of stone and cleaning trials employing methods selected on the basis of information from the assessment and analysis stages, was not an option in the St Mary's situation due to the pressure of the works programme. Variation in sequence of events was compensated for by increasing the number of trials undertaken and by taking of samples within the test areas before and after the trials. This modified approach proved very successful.

Characteristics and condition of the external masonry

Eras of masonry construction

The existing masonry of St Mary's, Gateshead, dates from Norman times through to the late nineteenth century (1874) when an extensive restoration programme was undertaken. The architectural style of each era of construction varied as did the general characteristics of the stones and jointing mortars used.

Petrographic analysis determined that, while there was a noticeable range of variations within the stones used from era to era, and also within the same era, the stone was essentially of the one type. The analytical

Figure 6.5 On the south elevation of St Mary's, Gateshead, heavily soiled, sound areas of masonry contrasted strongly with light-coloured, heavily weathered surfaces which were experiencing continual surface loss. These contrasts detracted from the architecture of the building as a whole.

work also confirmed the wide range of natural variations within individual stones. The stone of all the construction eras was classified as an argillaceous sandstone, a stone which was highly susceptible to water-related deterioration, frost and salt crystallization damage.

The stonework of St Mary's comprised heavily soiled black surfaces

Figure 6.6 Moderate and heavy soiling on the north elevation of St Mary's, Gateshead, gave this facade a more unified appearance than its southern counterpart. Areas of lightness again related to surfaces undergoing continuous granulation and loss.

contrasting with lightly soiled areas and areas of 'cleaned' stone where stones had lost their surfaces due to weathering. The visual contrast between the dark and light areas was so great as to be a distraction to the church's architecture.

The tower of St Mary's had the most widespread and most uniform expanse of dark soiling. At lower levels, soiling was heaviest within localized areas of heavy water saturation and where the stonework had not lost its original surface.

Older areas of masonry were not necessarily more heavily weathered.

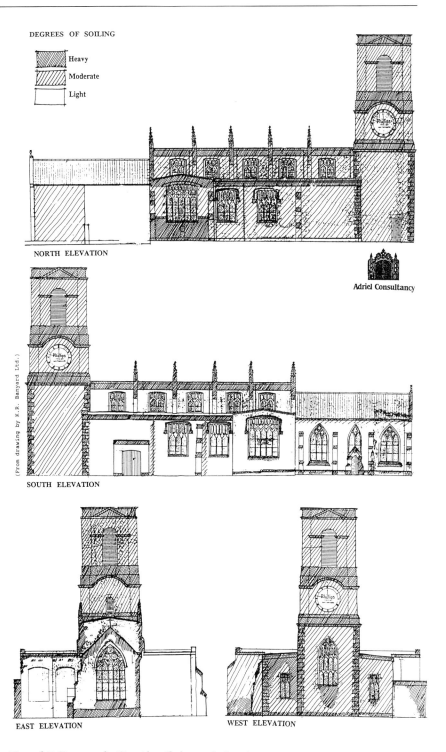

Figure 6.7 Degrees of soiling identified on each elevation.

Stone units in areas of very heavy water saturation and areas of greatest salt crystallization damage were in the worst condition.

Within each era of construction, the condition of the walling had been most greatly affected by the parlous condition of the joints. Cement-rich repointing mortars had caused deterioration of the adjacent stones and permitted water penetration. All areas would require the removal of the cementitious pointing mortars and the cutting out and repointing of the joints prior to cleaning. From the point of view of the cleaning, the condition of the joints was of greatest concern as regards the entry and freezing of water and the entry and retention of acidic and alkaline cleaning agents which were not rinsed out.

The decision to clean the external masonry of the church was evaluated from an aesthetic viewpoint and from a technical viewpoint. The effect that cleaning would have on the final appearance of the church was the main aesthetic consideration. It was, therefore, necessary to determine what level of cleaning could be achieved.

Proposed remedial works

At the time the cleaning study commenced, repointing and stone replacement works had commenced to the specification of the project architect. The visual disturbance of these was most noticeable within heavily soiled areas.

Repointed joints in areas of heavy soiling were very stark in appearance. Individual stones replaced on heavily soiled areas such as the tower, the clerestory parapets and the late nineteenth century porch were also visually prominent. If St Mary's was to be repaired and not cleaned, its uneven appearance, created by soiling and deterioration processes, would become more patchy as a result of the repairs.

On-site cleaning trials

Areas for the on-site trials were selected by Adriel Consultancy in conjunction with the Conservation Department, Gateshead Metropolitan Borough Council. Those on the northern elevation of the church were the least obtrusive of all the low-level masonry available, and were considered to be as representative as reasonably possible of the degrees of soiling seen elsewhere. They included masonry from the fourteenth,

Figure 6.8 Location of trial cleaning zones.

fifteenth, mid-eighteenth and mid-nineteenth centuries (see Figure 6.8). The areas of masonry selected were also considered to be as representative as reasonably possible of the surface and joint conditions seen throughout the building. Chemical, abrasive and low pressure water cleaning trials were undertaken within each test zone. The positions of all tests were marked on the drawings, along with the positions of samples taken for analysis. Details of materials and processes used were also recorded (see Figure 6.9).

All surfaces were inspected by eye and ×30 field microscope prior to application of any cleaning process or materials. Those to be involved in chemical cleaning were sampled so that pH and soluble salt contents prior to cleaning could be established.

Edges of test zones were defined by masking to enable direct comparison between cleaned and uncleaned surfaces within the same block. Joints were included within each zone in order to evaluate the effect of each cleaning process on arrises and pointing material. Each zone included a minimum of three courses, heavily soiled protrusions and plinth stones as well as lesser soiled ashlar.

The chemical trials involved products from the three main chemical manufacturers in operation at that time. Alkali–acid and acid-only processes were used. Cleaners in the form of liquids, gels and poultices were employed. Details of products used are shown in Figure 6.10.

TEST ZONE 'A'
SUMMARY OF TEST PROCEDURES

FOR ALL TEST AREAS:
Newlock products were applied and removed by a representative of the manufacturer. Neolith products were applied and removed and dry abrasive cleaning undertaken by the cleaning and surface repair contractor. A representative for the ProSoCo products could not attend on the day of the trials but had visited site and provided recommendations for products and dwell times.

A1:   Prewet
          Acidic gel (Newlock SC002B), dwell 15 minutes
          Acidic liquid (Newlock SC001), dwell 15 minutes, agitation, rinsed

A2:   Prewet
          Alkaline liquid (Newlock SC005), dwell 15 minutes, rinsed
          Acidic gel (Newlock SC002B), dwell 15 minutes, rinsed

A3:   Reference number not used

A4:   Thixotropic alkaline gel (coating remover) (ProSoCo Heavy Duty Paint Stripper), 24 hour dwell, extended rinse
          Acidic cleaner/neutraliser diluted (ProSoCo Restoration Cleaner, 3:1 water:product), 5 minute dwell, rinsed

A5:   Alkaline, clay-based poultice (ProSoCo T-1217 Poultice), covered for 24 hour dwell, rinsed
          Acidic cleaner/neutraliser diluted (ProSoCo Restoration Cleaner, 3:1 water:product), 5 minute dwell, rinsed, 2
          applications

A6a):   Prewet
          Thixotropic alkaline iquid (ProSoCo 766 Masonry Prewash), 30 minute dwell, extended rinse
          Acidic cleaner/neutraliser diluted (ProSoCo Heavy Duty Restoration Cleaner, 3:1 water:product), 7 minute dwell,
          rinsed

A6b):   Prewet
          Acidic cleaner only (ProSoCo Restoration Cleaner), 7 minute dwell, rinsed

A7a):   Prewet
          Alkaline liquid (Neolith HDL), 30 minute dwell, rinsed
          Acidic liquid cleaner/neutraliser (Neolith 625SS), 7 minute dwell, rinsed

A7b):   Prewet
          Acidic liquid cleaner (Neolith 625SS), 10 minute dwell, rinsed

A8a):   Dry air abrasive with olivine, 200 psi
          (Mainly rubble-faced blocks)

A8b):   Abrasive as for A8a) but with increased working distance

A8c):   Dry air abrasive with olivine, 200 psi
          Onto smooth surface of late 19th century buttress, with fine surface tooling
          At similar work distance to A8b)

A9:   Cutting out wide, cementitious pointing and patch mortars

A10:   Pressure water* only to area of black soiling

A11:   Pressure water* to area with surface organic growth and defective core, bedding and pointing mortars

A12:   Pressure water* to RHS of Area A9

* Fan tip nozzle, 750-1,000 psi at the nozzle, variable work distances not less than 250mm (10")
Ambient Temperature: c. 5°C
All rinsing done with cold water (hot water preferable in some circumstances but not available)

Figure 6.9 Test zone A – Details of materials and procedures.

St. Mary's Church, Gateshead
Masonry Cleaning Evaluation

Adriel Consultancy

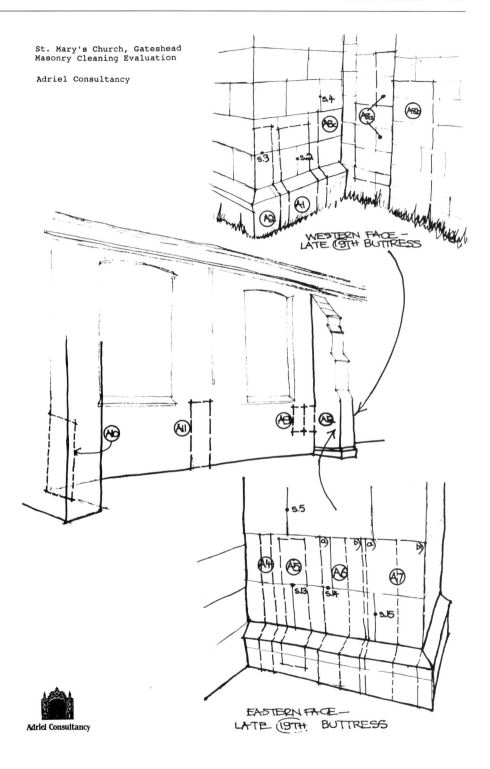

WESTERN FACE –
LATE 19TH BUTTRESS

EASTERN FACE –
LATE 19TH BUTTRESS

Adriel Consultancy

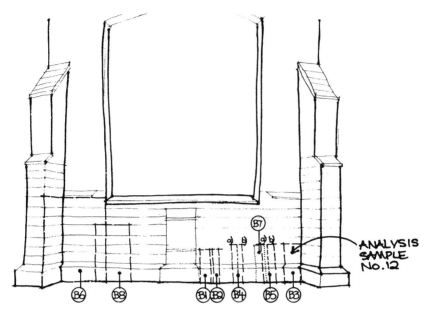

TEST ZONE 'B'
SUMMARY OF TEST PROCEDURES

FOR ALL TEST AREAS·
Newlock products were applied and removed by a representative of the manufacturer. Neolith products were applied and removed and dry abrasive cleaning undertaken by the cleaning and surface repair contractor. A representative for the ProSoCo products could not attend on the day of the trials but had visited site and provided recommendations for products and dwell times.

B1:   Alkaline, clay-based poultice (ProSoCo T-1217 Poultice), covered for 24 hour dwell, rinsed
        Acidic cleaner/neutraliser diluted (ProSoCo Restoration Cleaner, 3:1 water:product), 10 minute dwell, rinsed

B2:   Thixotropic alkaline paste (coating remover) (ProSoCo Heavy Duty Paint Stripper), 24 hour dwell, extended rinse
        Neutralisation and further cleaning as for B1

B3:   Prewet
        Thixotropic, acid-based paste (Newlock SC001B), 30 minute dwell, rinsed

B4a):   Prewet
        Thixotropic alkaline liquid (ProSoCo 766 Masonry Prewash), 30 minute dwell, rinsed
        Acidic cleaner/neutraliser diluted (ProSoCo Restoration Cleaner, 3:1 water:product), 5 minute dwell, rinsed

B4b):   Prewet
        Acidic cleaner as for B4a)

B5a):   Prewet
        Alkaline liquid (Neolith HDL), 30 minute dwell, rinsed
        Acidic cleaner/neutraliser (Neolith 625SS), 5-10 minute dwell, rinsed

B5b):   Prewet
        Acidic cleaner as for B5a)

B6:   Dry air abrasive (olivine abrasive), 200 psi

B7:   Dry air abrasive (olivine abrasive), 200 psi

B8:   Pressure water*

*Fan tip nozzle, 750-1,000 psi at the nozzle, variable working distances
Ambient temperature· c.5°C
All rinsing done with cold water (hot water not available)

Adriel Consultancy

Figure 6.9 Test zone B – Details of materials and procedures.

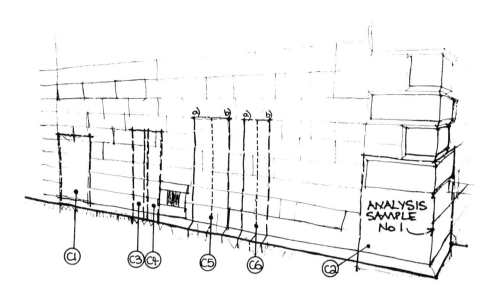

TEST ZONE 'C'
SUMMARY OF TEST PROCEDURES

FOR ALL TEST AREAS:
Newlock products were applied and removed by a representative of the manufacturer. Neolith products were applied and removed and dry abrasive cleaning undertaken by the cleaning and surface repair contractor. A representative for the ProSoCo products could not attend on the day of the trials but had visited site and provided recommendations for products and dwell times.

C1:   Prewet
        Thixotropic acid-based paste (Newlock SC005), 15 minute dwell, rinsed
        Acidic liquid (Newlock SC001), 15 minute dwell, agitation, rinsed

C2:   Thick alkaline gel (Newlock SC005B), 24 hour dwell, extended rinse
        Acidic cleaner/neutraliser (Newlock SC002B), 15 minute dwell, rinsed

C3:   Alkaline, clay-based poultice (ProSoCo T-1217 Poultice, covered for 24 hour dwell, extended rinse
        Acidic cleaner/neutraliser diluted (ProSoCo Restoration Cleaner, 3:1 water:product), 5 minute dwell, rinsed

C4:   Thixotropic alkaline paste (coating remmover)(ProSoCo Heavy Duty Paint Stripper), 24 hour dwell, extended
        rinse
        Neutralisation and cleaning as for C3

C5a):   Prewet
        Alkaline liquid (Neolith HDL), 30 minute dwell, rinsed
        Acidic cleaner/neutraliser (Neolith 625SS), 7 minute dwell, rinsed

C5b):   Prewet
        Acidic cleaner/neutraliser (Neolith 625SS), 10 minute dwell, rinsed

C6a):   Prewet
        Thixotropic alkaline liquid (ProSoCo 766 Masonry Prewash), 30 minute dwell, rinsed
        Acid cleaner/neutraliser diluted (ProSoCo Restoration Cleaner, 3:1 water:product), 5 minute dwell, rinsed

C6b):   Prewet
        Acid cleaner as for C6a)

* Fan tip nozzle, 750-1,000 psi at the nozzle, variable work distances not less than 250mm (10")
Ambient Temperature: c. 5°C
All rinsing done with cold water (hot water preferable in some circumstances but not available)

Adriel Consultancy

Figure 6.9 Test zone C – Details of materials and procedures.

PRODUCT INFORMATION

PRODUCT		MAIN ACTIVE INGREDIENT	pH
Newlock SC001	Acidic liquid	Hydrofluoric acid (HF)	1*
Newlock SC002B	Acidic gel	Hydrofluoric acid (HF)	1*
Newlock SC005	Alkaline liquid	Sodium hydroxide (NaOH)	14*
Newlock SC005B	Alkaline gel	Sodium hydroxide (NaOH)	14*
			* Assumed - value not stated on literature.
ProSoCo 766 Masonry Prewash		Sodium hydroxide (NaOH)	14
ProSoCo T-1217 Poultice		Sodium hydroxide (NaOH)	14
ProSoCo Heavy Duty Paint Stripper		Potassium hydroxide (KOH)	14
ProSoCo Restoration Cleaner		Hydrofluoric acid (HF)	1.2
ProSoCo Heavy Duty Restoration Cleaner, diluted 3:1, water:cleaner		Hydrofluoric acid (HF)	1.5
Neolith HDL		Sodium hydroxide	>13
Neolith 625SS		Hydrofluoric acid (HF)	<1

Figure 6.10 Proprietary product information.

Summary of test findings

The pressure water procedure was ineffective in removing soiling from sound surfaces. It was, however, effective in dislodging loose, cementitious mortar, portions of delaminated or granulated stone surface, and effective in rinsing out heavily weathered pointing and core mortars.

Test zone A9 included heavily weathered fourteenth century masonry which had no evidence of original surface tooling or profile. The surfaces of all the blocks were heavily granulated and superficial cementitious pointing covered substantial perimeter margins of each stone. Works began with the cutting out of all cementitous pointing mortars using hand-held tools and clearing of the loose and pulverized bedding and core mortar behind. Removal of the pointing alone presented a section

Figure 6.11 To some areas of masonry, a substantial proportion of cleaning was achieved simply by the cutting out of wide, superficial, cementitious pointing. (Test zone A9.)

of walling vastly improved in appearance to the untreated adjacent areas.

The area was then rinsed with low pressure water (350 psi at 12 in. working distance). Loose surface soiling was removed along with granulating and delaminating stone. No surface material other than that which would have weathered off in the immediate future was removed by the washing.

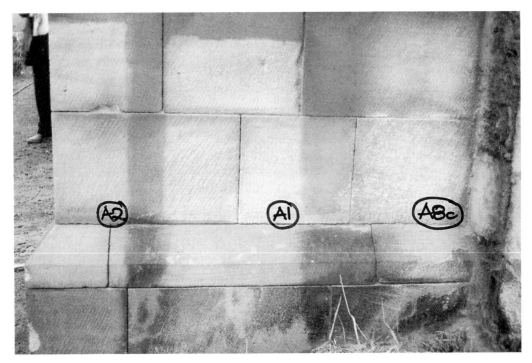

Figure 6.12 Areas A1 and A2 were cleaned chemically. The uneven clean of area A8c was achieved by an air abrasive process which proved to be too severe for the masonry at hand.

The final appearance of the stonework was considered successful, particularly when viewed from a distance and worthy of consideration as an acceptable, partially cleaned surface for this type and condition of masonry. The small areas of residual soiling prevented the stone from having a brand new appearance and were considered to be in keeping with its age and weathered character. From a technical point of view, their retention may not have been acceptable but represented only 10–15 per cent of the stone area. The processes adopted on this area of stonework would not be as successful on stonework which was in sounder condition.

The dry abrasive method proposed by the contractor was evaluated on both finely tooled and irregular faced ashlar. Despite many adjustments to the parameters of the processes, it was immediately obvious on each test area that the air abrasive cleaning would not be acceptable unless the equipment and abrasive supplied could be changed. On the flat, finely tooled surfaces, the surface loss happened very quickly and gun shading was caused readily. Irregular surfaces elsewhere required several passes of the abrasive stream in order to remove soiling from all the ledges. Damage was readily caused to the high spots.

Generally, the results of the chemical cleaning trials were the most

Figure 6.13 These two test zones revealed natural staining originating from the stone itself which would remain on much of the masonry surface on completion of cleaning. It is seen in the form of irregular grey bands on the tan colour of the body of the stone.

successful of the cleaning categories investigated. In areas of heavy and intransigent soiling, alkaline cleaners were found to be of little benefit in terms of removal of soiling, the acid-based cleaners doing most of the work. Product strength and dwell time were the criteria which determined the level of clean achieved by the acidic cleaners. In areas of moderate soiling, the most successful clean was achieved by the alkaline clay-based poultice followed by a dilute hydrofluoric acid-based cleaner (ProSoCo T-1217 Poultice and ProSoCo Restoration Cleaner).

The chemical-based trials undertaken in test zone C indicated clearly that full removal of soiling was not going to be possible from all sections of stonework. Most of the stones included harder bands which were darker in colour than the softer areas. Even within areas which achieved moderate and good levels of cleaning, it could be seen that considerable amounts of colour remained within the harder bands. Depth of the marking was 3–4 mm. Close inspection of stones suggested the colouring to have originated from within the stone itself and therefore to be part of its natural patina. Thin section analysis identified mineral sources of the colouring. Removal of the marking was considered inappropriate and impossible to achieve without widespread damage. It needed to be realized that certain amounts of colouring would remain within the stonework. In many ways this was desirable from an aesthetic point of view as the cleaned stonework would not appear 'new and cleaned' but rather 'aged and cleaned'.

On the basis of the cleaning works of test zone C, it could be said that a good level of clean (70 per cent approximately) would be achievable on the tower stonework with a use of two-step, alkali–acid cleaning process. The full success of this approach needed to be confirmed by the undertaking of larger trial areas on the tower itself, particularly on the upper levels involving both heavily soiled protrusions, as well as ashlar. Further details on the chemically cleaned trial areas is included in the following discussion on the results of the analysis programme.

The final assessment of the trial zones included:

1. Visual assessment of the cleaned and uncleaned stone surfaces when dry.
2. Inspection of the surfaces under ×30 field microscope in order to determine the level of clean achieved, the extent and nature of larger-scale loss or damage to the masonry surface and the impact of the materials and processes on the block arrises and joint materials. The stonework was also inspected for alterations including bleaching and the deposition of residues.
3. Within a representative selection of trial cleaning areas, samples of stonework were taken on completion of cleaning for comparison with uncleaned surfaces to establish the extent and nature of any deposits. This included the investigation of petrographic thin sections and the quantitative analysis of soluble salts.

The analysis programme

The analytical programme was aimed at analysis of a series of stone samples to provide important additional information regarding the stone constituents, properties and weathering processes under way and at providing additional information regarding the effect of chemical cleaning on the stone surfaces. An important thrust was to determine the mineralogy of the stone types present and whether this had altered as a result of weathering or due to the cleaning materials and procedures.

Seventeen samples were taken reflecting the various periods of construction of St Mary's, its materials and soiling. Samples removed from the walls reflected the observed decay and soiling patterns. The seven samples taken with regard to stone cleaned during the trials were removed by direct mechanical means within one hour of completion of the recommended procedures and bagged. Generally, discrete samples of loose stone fragments were removed rather than cores being taken. Seven of the test cleaning areas subjected to chemical cleaning were sampled and analysed for the presence of residual materials (see Tables 6.1 and 6.2).

Table 6.1 XRF analysis of whole samples

					Element detected				
Sample	Si	S	P	Ca	Ti	Fe	Mn	Cr	Cu
5	10.3	3.3	0.6	2.8	0.4	3.8	374*	441*	nd
6	8.4	7.8	nd	9.4	0.4	2.7	494*	499*	640*
7	11.8	2.4	0.7	1.9	0.4	5.9	863*	445*	537*
9	11.2	2.5	0.7	2.1	0.3	2.2	399*	724*	0.2
10	10.3	3.9	0.5	3.6	0.3	2.7	nd	447*	567*

Values are given as percentage weight relative to the whole sample (major elements) except as marked *
where the values are given as parts per million (minor/trace elements).
    The presence of $CaSO_4$, calcium sulphate, can be inferred from the amounts of Ca and S and a degree
of confirmation obtained by calculation. The table does *not say* $CaSO_4$ is the sulphate present.
Source: Lithan Ltd.

Petrographic analysis

Petrographic thin sections were prepared from seven samples which represented the various eras of construction. Photomicrographs and petrographic profiles which set out the observed mineralogy and texture of each of the samples are presented in Figures 6.14 and 6.15.

The petrographic analysis of all the samples indicated a series of rock

Table 6.2 Water soluble extract

Sample	Cations in ppm (mg/kg)					pH	Anions in ppm (mg/kg)			Percentage weight of salts
	Ca	Mg	Na	K	Fe		SO_4	NO_3	Cl	
1[a]	7,140	127	1,020	178	10	6.25	14,029	1,454	740	4.51
2[a]	8,137	58	153	178	<5	6.02	17,881	367	165	3.83
3[a]	5,675	24	615	118	10	4.98	12,932	70	156	2.39
4	7,297	40	201	176	44	5.80	14,214	793	284	2.10
5	9,736	53	211	132	6	5.62	19,836	1,329	305	3.47
6	17,869	60	265	201	20	5.22	38,178	609	381	6.72
7	6,565	535	413	316	<5	5.51	15,318	287	900	3.00
8	21,232	184	425	215	14	5.77	53,080	708	425	7.31
9	7,911	60	116	116	10	6.28	20,253	116	372	3.09
10	8,936	164	404	259	<5	5.68	19,889	2,163	749	3.60
12[a]	1,975	160	86	117	23	5.46	4,503	636	129	1.04
13[a]	11,753	19	601	191	<5	6.37	27,893	273	82	4.35
14[a]	1,159	13	839	105	<5	6.83	3,317	476	89	0.98
15[a]	125	7	414	119	<5	6.33	341	60	51	0.61
16[a]	895	240	246	157	<5	5.95	1,317	2,141	445	1.06

[a] Cleaned samples.
See comments beneath Table 6.1 regarding inferred and calculated information.
Source: Lithan Ltd.

types which were broadly similar in mineralogy and texture. All the rocks were generally classified as argillaceous sandstone. Clays were major constituents of the media binding the quartz grains. All samples had experienced progressive surface deterioration in the form of granulation (loss of binder) and subsurface microfractures. Another distinctive feature was the variation in the total and relative clay mineral content between inner and outer zones.

It was not possible to distinguish clearly between cleaned and uncleaned samples in terms of the removal of outer mineralogical components or increased porosity in outer layers. This was considered to speak favourably for the chemical processes tested. Several samples which had not been cleaned showed significant depletions in their outer layers. The reduction in clay mineralogy of one of the seven cleaned samples was virtually imperceptible and could not be unequivocally attributed to the cleaning processes. The cleaning process adopted had used a hydrofluoric acid-based product believed to be amongst the strongest on the market. It had been included in the trials as it was one of the chemical cleaners the contractor was proposing to use. An additional reason for taking the sample from this area was that from a visual assessment it appeared that the colour of the stone had been altered by the hydrofluoric acid-based cleaning process.

The thin sections taken from cleaned areas also revealed that the surfaces which had been assessed by eye to be clean still retained remnants of soiling in crevices but had experienced no alteration to the binder constituents. This confirmed that chemical alteration of the stone was not likely to be caused when procedures were adopted which achieved a level of clean considered complete on the basis of close visual assessment, the criterion universally adopted on sites.

Chemical analysis

This phase of analytical work was directed towards determining the total chemistry of stone samples representative of the test cleaning areas, as well as locations not involved in the cleaning trials.

All stone samples taken were analysed to determine water and acid-soluble components using inductively coupled plasma spectroscopy (ICP) and ion chromatography (IC) (see Table 6.2). The acidic components were also tested but the results were negligible. The total chemistry of five samples of uncleaned stone was prepared by X-ray fluorescence (XRF) which established the general types and quantities of soluble salts present (see Table 6.1). It determined the high inherent

PETROGRAPHIC PROFILE

Site: St. Mary's Church, Gateshead
Date: November, 1990

A: SURFACE OBSERVATIONS

1	Pollutant crust	Absent
2	Organic matter	Present
3	Treatment residues	None seen
4	Metallic stain	Absent
5	Efflorescence	Absent
6	Sound	Yes

B: COLOUR OF HAND SPECIMEN

1	Outer	
2	Inner	
3	Comment:	small sample

C: GRAIN TEXTURE

1	Shape:	rounded to subangular
2	Contacts:	point and face
3	Sorting:	moderate
4	Porosity:	estimated 10%
5	Very coarse	>1.0mm
6	Coarse	.5-1.0mm
7	Medium	.25-.5mm - main
8	Fine	.125-.25mm
9	Very fine	<.125mm

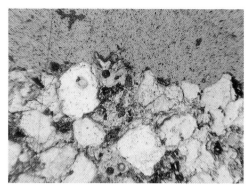

Photomicrograph of sample 1.
Photographed at ×60 magnification, plain
polarized light. (Lithan Ltd)

D: MINERALOGY

1	Major constituents	>10% vol: Quartz, Clays
2	Minor constituents	2-10% vol: Ore minerals, Lithic fragments, Feldspars, Mica
3	Other constituents	<2% vol: Calcite to outer surface

E: CEMENTATION

1 Type: Clays
2 Degree: Variable

F: DECOMPOSITION PRODUCTS

NA

G: DISCUSSION

A poorly defined orientation is present and the degree of cohesion varies within the section dependent upon point contacts and
the interstitial Clays, primarily Kaolinite. The Micas are larger than Sample 9, occurring as distinct grains in addition to those
interstitially as before. A zone of mineral enrichment occurs and a system of micro-fractures extends through the section parallel
to the surface. This is an Argillaceous sandstone.
Prepared by Lithan Ltd

Figure 6.14 Petrographic analysis of sample 1, corner of quoin to mid-eighteenth century masonry. Sample taken
within test zone C2, cleaned by HF-based acid product only. Sound body of stone and residual soiling to outer layer
can be identified.

PETROGRAPHIC PROFILE

Site: St. Mary's Church, Gateshead
Date: November, 1990

Photomicrograph of sample 12.
Photographed at ×60 magnification, plain
polarized light. (Lithan Ltd)

A: SURFACE OBSERVATIONS

1	Pollutant crust	Present
2	Organic matter	Present
3	Treatment residues	None seen
4	Metallic stain	Absent
5	Efflorescence	Absent
6	Sound	No

B: COLOUR OF HAND SPECIMEN

1	Outer	
2	Inner	
3	Comment:	small sample

C: GRAIN TEXTURE

1	Shape: _	angular to rounded
2	Contacts:	point and face
3	Sorting:	moderate to poor
4	Porosity:	estimated 10%
5	Very coarse	>1.0mm
6	Coarse	.5-1.0mm
7	Medium	.25-.5mm - main
8	Fine	.125-.25mm
9	Very fine	<.125mm

D: MINERALOGY

1	Major constituents	>10% vol: Quartz, Clays
2	Minor constituents	2-10% vol: Ore minerals, Lithic fragments, Feldspars, Mica
3	Other constituents	<2% vol:

E: CEMENTATION

1 Type: Clays
2 Degree: Variable

F: DECOMPOSITION PRODUCTS

   NA

G: DISCUSSION

The section is similar to the previous sections and is differentiated by a decrease in the Kaolinite and an increase in the ore minerals. This is an Argillaceous sandstone.

Prepared by Lithan Ltd

Figure 6.15 Petrographic analysis of sample 12, from within area of fifteenth century stonework after cleaning with HF acid-based gel (test zone B3). Bleaching, suspected following visual assessment, was not confirmed.

contaminant salt loading of the stone and enabled assessments as to whether further salts had been deposited by the cleaning processes.

Inherent contaminants

The stonework was found to be carrying an extremely high loading of soluble salts which derived principally from direct deposition and interaction with atmospheric pollutants. While these had interacted very little with the mineralogy of the stone, a reaction was found to have taken place between the mineralogy and the existing cementitious pointing and bedding mortars. Investigation of uncleaned stone samples revealed the presence of other contaminants of varying degrees of water solubility, including calcite, again derived from the mortars and representing a source of physical decay additional to the general physico-chemical decay caused by the water soluble components. The data of Table 6.2 also showed that a suite of minerals was present as contaminants in addition to the ubiquitous gypsum.

Contaminants from the chemical cleaning trials

The areas in which the first stage of cleaning was undertaken using alkaline materials were found to contain significantly higher sodium (Na) levels when compared with uncleaned samples of the same stone or other samples cleaned without alkaline materials. Small residues of the alkaline cleaning materials were clearly being left in the stonework.

The pH values established indicated that either neutralization of the alkaline component was not carried out and that acid residues remained in the stone or that the cleaning was not effective. Information from the petrographic analysis supported the latter argument: it de-emphasized the product-related contaminant argument problem but did not eliminate it.

The cleaning procedures were found to mobilize the existing salt content, i.e. the salts that had been introduced over time but were not inherent to the original stone. The results also confirmed that the stonework would be left with a very substantial salt loading following cleaning. It was concluded that the cleaning processes tested could not be expected greatly to improve the inherent salt loading problem of the stonework, although some salts would be removed during rinsing procedures. If it were to be undertaken, reduction in soluble salts levels would need to be achieved by means other than the cleaning, e.g. plain clay poulticing.

It was recognized that the low ambient temperatures of the trial period reduced the effectiveness of all the cleaning compounds and the use of cold water washes (hot water was not available) had reduced the effectiveness of the rinsing of residues, particularly of alkaline products for which it would have been preferred. The use of hot water would also have improved the amounts of inherent salts washed from the masonry surfaces. It was also advised at the time of the trials that the rinse procedures adopted were too fast and too short to be effective.

On the basis of findings of both the petrographic and chemical analysis it was determined that removal of the surface soiling to the masonry was still desirable from the point of view of reducing the effect of indurated layers and crusts inhibiting moisture movement at the stone face, limiting salt dispersal to the evaporation surface.

Previous treatments

While the observed decay patterns of some areas of the St Mary's masonry suggested that a chemical treatment had been applied to the stone surface, samples selected for analysis and investigated using infra-red spectroscopy failed to show the presence of any coating which could be classified as either linseed oil or silicone or other such material.

Physical analysis

Two fist-sized lumps of stone taken from the side of the pilaster to the fifteenth century masonry on the north elevation, were investigated to determine the physical parameters of the main stone types observed.

Physical parameters

The effective porosity, total porosity, water absorption coefficient, saturation coefficient and density of the samples were determined. The results are presented in Table 6.3.

Table 6.3 The physical parameters

Sample	Effective porosity N_e (%)	Total porosity N_t (%)	Water absorption coefficient W (%)	Saturation coefficient S	Density D (Kg/M^3)
11a	11.8	14.3	4.7	0.83	2,287
11b	11.8	15.5	5.0	0.76	2,157

Source: Lithan Ltd.

The data confirmed the textural differences and similarities observed in the petrographic thin sections and hand specimens. The combined results revealed characteristics which meant that the ingress of water and waterborne contaminants to the stones was easy. The stones were also found to be very susceptible to physical disruption caused by freeze–thaw cycles or the hydration–dehydration cycles of water-soluble salts. These findings were considered applicable to the stonework of the church generally because of the close correlation of other factors. The findings were particularly relevant as they confirmed why cleaning operations involving water should not be undertaken in periods of low ambient temperatures.

The decision to clean

The following is a summary of the technical and aesthetic considerations which provided the basis for the decision to clean.

Abrasive cleaning methods tested during the trial period were generally not suitable for the cleaning of the St Mary's Church masonry. The method demonstrated by the contractor did not prove successful on any of the types of surface soiling assessed. If this method of cleaning were to be pursued, additional trials with different abrasives and different equipment would have been required. The building programme did not permit this.

During the trials, water pressure at about 1000 psi demonstrated value in removing loose surface material and cutting out loose pointing but not adherent soiling.

The chemical cleaning processes investigated during the on-site trials gave a range of visual results which varied depending on the age, type and condition of the masonry and the degrees of adherent soiling. None of the materials tested offered significant advantage over the others from a residue point of view. While the analysis did not detect damage to any of the surfaces cleaned by chemical means, areas which appeared 'over-cleaned' could be seen to have experienced minor surface losses on a scale too large to be accommodated by the analytical process used. Several processes were of necessity rejected.

All processes which involved the application of an alkaline pre-wash in liquid, gel or poultice form indicated some residual deposition of product-related soluble salts. Chemical cleaning trials involving acid alone recorded deposition of small amounts of residues related to these products. The quantities of these were very small, especially when compared with the existing salt loading. It was considered possible that the levels of sulphates detected could have been reduced signficantly if hot water had been used for the rinsing procedures, the rinse times had been extended and the trial work had been undertaken at a higher ambient temperature. The problem could therefore be readily minimized and probably eliminated during larger-scale works if correct procedures were adopted.

By necessity, all the chemical cleaning trials involved the wetting and rinsing of the stonework on more than one occasion. This was found to have caused mobilization of the inherent salts, drawing some salts from deep within the stone up to the surface.

The depth of the soluble salt reservoir within the masonry was not fully determined. It was suspected it would be extensive and deep due to the extended and widespread water penetration of joints and the subsequent percolation of moisture.

On a large scale, the existing salt levels in the stonework could have been reduced using hot water (less than 95°C) rinsing and the brushing off of resultant efflorescence. For small areas of carved and moulded work which are at risk, the surfaces could be wetted, then coated with packs based on deionized water and clay into which salts would be drawn (analytical work at the surface and at depth would be necessary before and after each process to establish by how much the salt levels were being reduced). The effect and value of the above processes could only be fully determined if the reduction in salts could be measured. Any reduction would nevertheless be of benefit.

While it could not be said that technical reasons exist as to why the building should *not* be cleaned, it had also to be said that the use of chemical cleaning products in the St Mary's situation, if undertaken responsibly, would present only minor negative technical implications. The St Mary's masonry had greater problems, including its inherent salt loading, the condition of its pointing, bedding and core mortars, the localized weathering of beds within stones, the advanced weathering of individual blocks, and the possible lack of structural integrity to heavily weathered areas of walling.

It was also noted that while the stone surfaces would benefit from the removal of the black pollutant soiling, the on-site test and analysis showed that it could not be completely removed.

From an aesthetic viewpoint, the effect of the proposed cleaning revolved around what the likely appearance of the church would be and whether it would retain historic character. The areas of heaviest and darkest soiling were those which were visually most prominent. Their contrast with the remaining areas of masonry, particularly the lightly soiled areas, was strong. The dark soiling in these areas hid the detail of the architectural features.

An important finding of the trials was that the cleaning of moderately and heavily soiled masonry would remove only part of the soiling, leaving the surfaces looking less soiled but still aged. The starkness of the contrast between the lightly soiled areas and the moderately and

Figure 6.16 South elevation of St Mary's Church, Gateshead, on completion of cleaning and surface repair.

heavily soiled areas would be reduced if the latter too were cleaned. The lightly soiled areas of masonry contained a high proportion of blocks with granulating and delaminating surfaces and the occasional sound block which was heavily soiled. When viewed at a distance, the overall appearance of the masonry was fairly even. There was little purpose to be served by cleaning the whole of these areas because of the low level of soiled blocks within them.

Recommended cleaning methods and associated remedial works

1. It was recommended that the areas of carved detail such as hood mouldings and associated label stops were consolidated prior to cleaning in order to reduce the loss of detail. Many of these details were in very friable condition. Further laboratory trials were recommended to ensure selection of the correct consolidant and to confirm the nature and degree of its effect on the properties and behaviour of the stone.

2. Due to the heavy soiling on areas of carved detail, the cleaning process recommended was the alkaline clay-based poultice (ProSoCo T-1217, pH 14) and associated acidic neutralizer (ProSoCo Restoration Cleaner, undiluted, pH 1.2). These materials and procedures would give a greater degree of control for the cleaning of these localized areas. The analysis had confirmed that the iron in the stone was not generally in a form which would react readily with these cleaning compounds. The pressure at which the products were to be rinsed off was to be considerably lower than that used on ashlar, cornices and more robust surfaces elsewhere.

A detailed specification for the works was prepared and the works undertaken soon after.

The finished result

As predicted, an even level of clean could not be achieved. Residual soiling was greatest in areas where the most intense soiling had been. The overall impression of the cleaning was of an old masonry structure which had been treated respectfully. Good reduction in different intensities of soiling was achieved, even on the south elevation, and has served to integrate the appearance of each elevation and the building as a whole.

The value of the specialist investigations was proved. The quality of the cleaning and surface repair works which brought the theory into reality are a very significant part of the success of the project.

6.3 CASE STUDY 3: FACULTY OF ART AND DESIGN, BIRMINGHAM – THE CLEANING OF A COMPLEX VICTORIAN BUILDING

Background and brief

The Faculty of Art and Design, located in central Birmingham, is an imposing three-storey building designed by architects Martin and Chamberlain, and constructed in 1884 by Messrs Sapcote and Son. The Gothic design of its three street frontages exploits to the full the intricate combinations of buff and red sandstones, limestone, brick, red and buff terracottas, glazed and unglazed tiles, and mosaics. While the architectural effect of these materials was undoubtedly impressive, cleaning of the external surfaces was to be a complex operation as a result. Many of the difficulties and dangers that may have been encountered were avoided by the undertaking of a logical sequence of trials and investigations prior to preparation of the cleaning specifications for the main contract.

Architects for the project were Associated Architects of St Paul's Square, Birmingham. The client was the University of Central England in Birmingham. The specialist technical input into the cleaning procedures was provided by Adriel Consultancy, Nottingham. Main contractor for the works was William Sapcote and Son, Birmingham. The cleaning subcontractor was Aqua Cleaning Company, Birmingham. The success of the project must attributed to the strong team approach that was developed between these parties.

Cleaning was a necessary prerequisite to the surface repair programme. The architects had found it difficult to finalize the extent of necessary repairs as a result of the intensity of soiling in many areas. The facades had not been cleaned before and many of the surfaces were so heavily soiled that it was difficult to identify the substrate or to appreciate its condition, even where surfaces were inspected at close range. In its position at the centre of the city, the Faculty of Art and

Figure 6.17 South-east corner of the Faculty of Art and Design, Birmingham, prior to cleaning and surface repair. Intense soiling to sandstone surfaces masked their wealth of intricate detail. Colours of all other materials were strongly muted.

Design was surrounded by other buildings of similar scale, all of which had been cleaned, some on more than one occasion. Motivation for cleaning was also strong from a townscape point of view.

Figure 6.18 Detail of archway and gable to the main entrance. The foliated medallion and panels are of a Bath limestone and the lattice in between, encaustic tile. The highly carved gable above and archway beneath are of the light buff sandstone used widely on all facades.

On-site cleaning trials

Initial selection of methods

Initial deliberation as to which cleaning materials and methods would be suitable to on-site investigation resulted in the following conclusions:

1. Water washing would not clean the bulk of the facade materials.
2. The wide range of materials, surface characteristics and types made the use of abrasive cleaning impossible to undertake without significant damage on many of the surfaces even with frequent modifications to equipment and abrasive supply. Selective use of abrasive cleaning would have provided a gargantuan masking and protection problem as surfaces which may have been suited to it were dotted over the facades. While the use of small-scale air abrasive may have reduced or eliminated these concerns, the cost would have been very high. Abrasive cleaning was not discounted totally but it was decided that other methods should be investigated first.
3. In general terms, chemical cleaning processes were considered more suited to the combination of plain and ornate surfaces used. The success of their use would depend on identification of

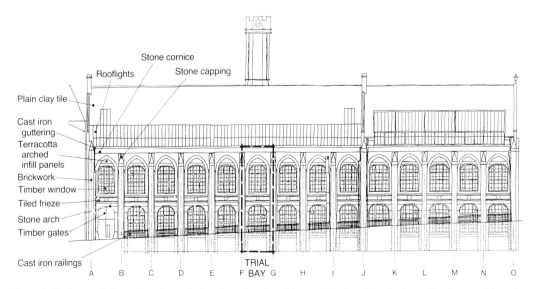

Figure 6.19 Cornwall Street (north west) elevation, Faculty of Art and Design, Birmingham, facade materials and location of the trial cleaning bay.

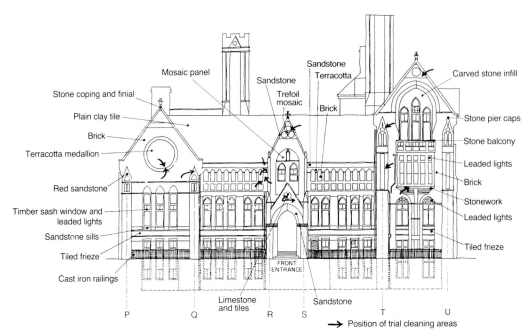

Figure 6.20 Margaret Street (south west) elevation, Faculty of Art and Design, Birmingham, facade materials and location of trial cleaning areas.

the materials in each portion of all the elevations, very careful application and removal, and a relatively high proportion of protective measures for openings and small areas of incompatible materials. A range of processes was selected for on-site investigation.

First phase of on-site trials

On-site investigations began on the Cornwall Street elevation which was made up of fifteen bays of similar design and deployment of masonry types. A specification was drawn up for the undertaking of spot cleaning trials to be followed by the cleaning of a full-height bay with the preferred materials. Chemicals from the two manufacturers were evaluated on opposite sides of the test bay in order to reduce the chance of cross-contamination of rinse waters.

The predominant material of each bay was brickwork. Buff sandstone had been used for the gutter cornice, buttress slopes and the window sills. The decorative band to the first floor transome comprised glazed and unglazed tiles with a central rosette in limestone. The bays included the most widely used material types. The protection required for the

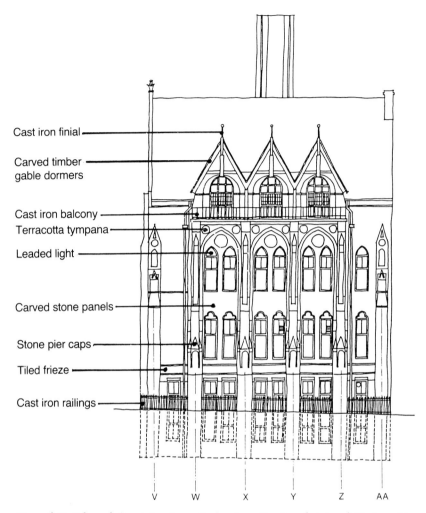

Figure 6.21 Edmund Street (south east) elevation, Faculty of Art and Design, Birmingham, facade materials.

tiles, rosette and the window could also be evaluated. Unfortunately, the evaluation procedures of the study were not able to incorporate a full range of analytical work prior to the trials. Nevertheless, a practical level of analysis was undertaken at essential points as work progressed, i.e. pH testing of surfaces and qualitative analysis of efflorescences.

The constituents and characteristics of the buff sandstone were identified by thin section analysis. This work revealed constituents of the stone to be the source of residual staining.[1]

Within the test bay, the areas selected for spot trials are shown in Figure 6.22. They were:

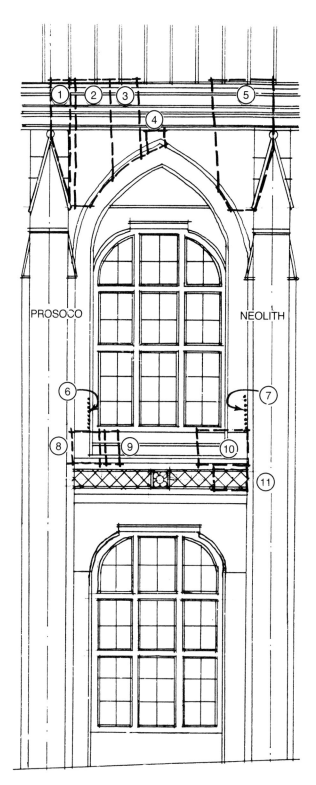

Figure 6.22 Location of spot trial areas to trial cleaning bay, bay 6 of the Cornwall Street elevation. Details of materials and processes are set out in Tables 6.4 and 6.5.

Gutter level (test area A)

- Portion of gutter cornice (sandstone, water saturated, soiled and stained).
- Side of buttress including sloping water tables (sandstone, heavy soiling, blotchy soiling).
- Heavily soiled brickwork adjacent to buttress, including unglazed terracotta moulding.
- The terracotta panel within the arch of the first-floor window was considered in too friable a condition for any general cleaning process. There was extensive evidence of decay due to the presence of soluble salts with many areas exfoliating in flakes up to 1 mm thick. The cleaning contractor was asked to record the panel photographically prior to any work elsewhere and to protect the panel to prevent any water or cleaning chemicals coming into contact with the surface. Specialist conservator advice would be necessary for the treatment of the fifteen different sculptured panels found at this height of the building.

Transome level (test area B)

- Portion of sloping sill, including end stooling (sandstone, moderate/blotchy soiling).
- Brick to window reveal (moderate soiling).
- A section of the tiled panel (light soiling).
- The limestone feature within the tiled panel (heavy soiling).

Fully sheeted scaffold to the width and height of the test bay remained in position until after the areas had dried and been evaluated.

The cleaning trials were undertaken in August 1990 at the end of a long, hot summer (by British standards). Representatives of the cleaning materials manufacturers were in attendance during the undertaking of their representative areas. Details of materials and processes used are set out in Table 6.4 and Table 6.5.

The appearance of all the completed trial cleaning areas did not necessarily represent the final appearance of the cleaned surfaces. The principal requirement was that the materials should be used as gently as possible. It was considered preferable that a surface be under-cleaned rather than over-cleaned and damaged.

The test areas were inspected visually with a ×30 field microscope and tested with pH strips while still damp and when dry. The following criteria were considered for each area:

Table 6.4 Products and processes used on test areas

Test area	Products and processes
1. Buff sandstone gutter cornice and water table	(a) ProSoCo T-1217 Poultice Dwell time 24 hours Bulk removed with plastic scrapers Pressure water rinse at 350 psi (b) ProSoCo Restoration Cleaner diluted 2 water : 1 cleaner Dwell time 5 minutes Pressure water rinse as above 90–95% clean achieved except for residual soiling to upward facing slopes of water table
2. Buff sandstone gutter cornice and orange brickwork beneath, including moulded brick to arch. Cornice and brickwork affected by extended period of saturation due to defective cast iron gutter above	(a) Pre-wet ProSoCo 766 Masonry Prewash Dwell time 20 minutes Rinsed as above (b) ProSoCo Restoration Cleaner diluted 2 water : 1 cleaner Dwell time 5 minutes Rinsed 90–95% clean on brickwork 80–85% clean on sandstone Water staining to gutter stone became apparent on drying out Algal growth reappeared within 10 days
3. Buff sandstone gutter cornice and orange brickwork beneath, including moulded brick to arch. Cornice and brickwork affected by extended period of saturation due to defective cast iron gutter above	(a) Pre-wet ProSoCo 766 Masonry Prewash Dwell time 20 minutes Rinsed as above (b) ProSoCo Limestone Afterwash, diluted 1 : 1 Dwell time 5 minutes Rinsed 75–80% clean to stone and brick and surfaces Water staining and algal regrowth as for area 2
4. Brickwork and moulded brick to arch	Test abandoned for reasons of cross-contamination
5. Buff sandstone gutter cornice and orange brickwork beneath, including moulded brick to arch. Cornice and brickwork affected by extended period of saturation due to defective cast iron gutter above	(a) Pre-wet Neolith HDL to sandstone and brickwork Dwell time 4 hours Pressure water rinse at 1200 psi (b) Brick: Neolith 600 Dwell time 10 minutes Stone to buttress: Neolith 625SS and 625HD Dwell times 10 minutes approximately 100% cleaning of brickwork Degree of clean to sandstone similar to area 1 Inherent staining not removed even though stronger acidic products used Surface roughening and arris damage very noticeable

6. Plain and moulded
    brickwork to window
    reveal

(a) Pre-wet
     ProSoCo 766 Masonry Prewash
     Dwell time 20 minutes
     Low pressure water rinse at 350 psi
(b) ProSoCo Restoration Cleaner diluted 2 water :
       1 cleaner
     Dwell time 5 minutes
     Rinse as above
90% clean achieved

7. Plain and moulded
    brickwork to window
    reveal

(a) Pre-wet
     Neolith HDL
     Dwell time 2½ hours
     Pressure rinsing at 1200 psi
(b) Neolith 600
     Dwell time 10 minutes
     Pressure rinsing as above
100% clean

8. Sandstone, sill and
    stooling to first floor
    window

(a) Pre-wet
     ProSoCo 766 Masonry Prewash
     Dwell time 45 minutes
     Pressure rinse at 350 psi
(b) ProSoCo Restoration Cleaner
     diluted 2 water : 1 cleaner
     Dwell time 5 minutes
     Rinsed as above
70–75% clean achieved after one application. (a) and
(b) repeated at dwell times of 30 minutes and 5 minutes
(2 water : 1 cleaner) respectively
90–95% clean
Residual soiling to areas of sandstone most heavily saturated
by weathering and where original surface remained

9. Sandstone sill to first
    floor window

(a) ProSoCo T-1217 Poultice
     As for test area 1
(b) ProSoCo Restoration cleaner diluted 2 water :
       1 cleaner; as for test area 1
95% clean apart from inherent residual soiling

10. Sandstone, sill and
     stooling to first floor
     window

(a) Pre-wet
     Neolith HDL
     Dwell Time 2½ hours
     Pressure rinse at 1200 psi
(b) Neolith 625SS and Neolith 625HD
     Dwell times 10 minutes approximately
     Rinsed, as above
100% cleaning of stone achieved
Inherent staining not removed, even though stronger acid
products used
Surface roughening and arris damage very noticeable

11. Tiled frieze and rosette

Glazed and unglazed tile: pre-wet
Vulpex soap in warm water, 1 : 6, applied and agitated with
natural bristle brushes
Rinsed 85% clean achieved and no further glaze loss
Derbyshire limestone rosette: thick soiling very slow to
respond to water softening and small scale brushing

The tests were undertaken to the recommendations of representatives of the product manufacturers.

Table 6.5 Details of products used

Product	Main active ingredient	pH
Neolith HDL	Sodium hydroxide (NaOH)	>13
Neolith 600	Hydrofluoric acid (HF)	<1
Neolith 625SS	Hydrofluoric acid (HF)	<1
Neolith 625HD	Hydrofluoric acid (HF)	<1
ProSoCo T-1217 Poultice	Sodium hydroxide	14
ProsoCo 766 Masonry Prewash	Sodium hydroxide	14
ProsoCo Limestone Afterwash	Acetic acid	1.6
ProsoCo Restoration Cleaner	Hydrogen fluoride (HF)	1.2

1. The level of clean achieved.
2. The evenness of the clean and the resultant appearance of the cleaned surface close up and at distance.
3. The effect on the masonry surface and its joints in terms of colour change, surface loss and deposition of residues.
4. The complexity of each of the cleaning systems.
5. The ease of usage of each of the systems and the operational implications of these.
6. The cost implications of the systems used.
7. The health and safety requirements.

Evaluation of the areas

Test area A (gutter level)

The materials of both suppliers performed similarly well on the heavy soiling of the brickwork, one more readily producing a cleaner and brighter surface (the products were stronger and the dwell times longer). In both areas, the surfaces of the bricks and joints were not affected by the processes. Efflorescence which appeared on all surfaces following trials developed along the tide mark which represented the extent of saturation from the gutter above. Semi-quantitative salt analysis indicated that the emerging salts were cleaning product related to a very minor extent only.

The comparative water absorption rates of the brickwork before and after the cleaning were evaluated with a Rilem tube. The rate after cleaning greatly exceeded that of before, indicating the effect that the soiling was having on the brick surfaces. Removal of the soiling therefore greatly increased the bricks' ability to release its inherent salt loading which lead to the bulk of efflorescence observed. The thorough pre-wetting regime had encouraged their emergence, inadvertently causing a desalination programme to take place.

A satisfactory level of clean could not be achieved on the brickwork using the acetic acid-based neutralizer. The system selected for the second phase of the trials was ProSoCo 766 Masonry Prewash (20 minute dwell), followed by Restoration Cleaner diluted with 2 parts water (5 minute dwell, repeated once if necessary).

Figure 6.23 View down onto a buff sandstone gable on completion of a spot trial using the alkaline poultice/acidic afterwash process selected for these surfaces. Areas of residual soiling also denote areas which have experienced least surface loss due to weathering.

Figure 6.24 Trial cleaning bay to Cornwall Street elevation on completion, with efflorescence in full bloom.

Both chemical cleaning systems achieved a good level of clean on the sandstone gutter cornice, revealing the water staining beneath as had been anticipated. It was suspected that there was perhaps more surface loss with one process than the other as considerably higher rinse pressures were used, but, as the surfaces were very weathered before the trials, this could not be confirmed.

The best cleaning result was achieved with the ProSoCo T-1217 Poultice/dilute Restoration Cleaner process which produced a superior result to the liquid cleaners with no visually observable surface loss. This process also performed best on the sandstone weatherings of the buttress and the sill at first-floor level.

Generally, the cleaning of the sloping areas of the sandstone proved problematic. It is normal and usually acceptable for some soiling originating from the stone itself to remain on areas of stone which have been heavily saturated throughout their life. Because the stone of the Faculty of Art and Design was so light in colour, small amounts of residual soiling were noticeable when viewed at close range. At a distance, the residual soiling was far less noticeable.

Thin section analysis identified the stone to be a porous, medium-grained sandstone, mainly composed of quartz with minor amounts of feldspars, mica and the clay mineral kaolinite. Abundant amounts of iron minerals were also identified. These accounted for the surface staining which was made up of large concentrations of oxyhydroxides present to a depth of 1 mm into the stone. An extensive series of laboratory tests were unable to remove the staining and it had to be concluded that, if its removal was necessary, it would have to be undertaken mechanically.[1]

The terracotta panels were excluded from the cleaning trials because of the friable condition of their moulded surfaces due to salt crystallization damage.

Test area B (transome level)
At the transome level, the liquid cleaners of both manufacturers performed similarly well on the brickwork and its joints. There was a high level of efflorescence on the ProSoCo panel which appeared to be product-related (brush marks were identifiable in the efflorescence pattern). The cause of this was believed to be the contact time of the alkaline cleaner (almost twice that used in test area A where minimal product-related efflorescence was detected. The following options were investigated during the test cleaning of the full bay:

1. Reduction in the contact time of the alkaline cleaner in line with that used on the brickwork of area A.
2. Reducing the dilution of the acidic afterwash from 2 : 1 to 1 : 1.
3. Using two neutralizing washes rather than one.
4. Controlling the volume of water used for pre-wetting.

The spot trial cleaning of the sandstone sill at first-floor level provided the same problems with residual staining as had been experienced on the buttress weatherings.

Conclusions (first phase)

At the end of the spot trials, it was concluded that, as far as the cleaning of brickwork was concerned, the materials of both suppliers performed similarly well on the brickwork but not on the stonework. The ProSoCo system demonstrated a considerably better overall result in the latter instance. An interim specification for the cleaning of the full bay using these products was prepared for costing and execution.

The procedures and results of the spot trial were recorded in a report which included a photographic record.

Cleaning the first elevation

The final specification for the Cornwall Street elevation was prepared only once the cleaning and evaluation of the trial bay were complete. During the cleaning of this elevation, the main problem was efflorescence on the brickwork.

Levels had been greatly reduced by modifications to the early specification, but, even so, the residual amounts were unacceptable. As has been mentioned, samples of efflorescence were sent for analysis and confirmed that the cleaning products were at fault to a very small extent, if at all. Additional precautions taken included the installation of plastic 'skirts' at first-floor sill level, to reduce the amount of run-off affecting brickwork beneath. In addition, as the surfaces dried out, efflorescence was removed twice a week using an industrial vacuum cleaner with a soft brush attachment. This provided an effective method of removing the salts and containing them prior to disposal.

Efflorescence continued to emerge for four weeks after the cleaning was completed. Trial areas of chemical efflorescence treatment were undertaken on a section of brickwork which had been particularly heavily affected. The reduction of efflorescence achieved was undeniably significant but reluctance to use the treatment remained. It was eventually agreed that the treatment should be used on selected areas of heavy efflorescence immediately prior to the striking of the scaffold, whilst the remainder and bulk of the surfaces were left to be resolved by the rinsing processes of the weather.

Cleaning the second elevation

The Margaret Street elevation, the principal facade of the Faculty of Art and Design, was the next to be cleaned. The Margaret Street elevation faced south-west and was more intensely weathered and soiled than the Cornwall Street elevation (north-west facing) had been. Much of the experience of the first elevation could be transferred to the second facade, and further spot testing was undertaken to confirm this and establish any minor adjustments. Additional testing was required on the foliated cream-coloured terracotta of a large medallion to the main gable, the colonnade of ornate red terracotta panels, red sandstone (Red Mansfield)

Figure 6.25 Many of the special architectural features of the Margaret Street elevation, fabricated in terracotta, included the cream coloured medallion and the red colonnade surrounds. Spot trials were conducted on each of these areas and a different cleaning specification was required in each instance.

Figure 6.26 Spot cleaning trial on the Margaret Street elevation being undertaken on buff sandstone, red terracotta and brickwork just below roof level.

which had been used to a limited degree to complement the red terracotta, buff sandstone tracery surrounding mosaic panels (the mosaics had recently been restored) and the foliated limestone and encaustic tile infill to the main entrance gable. The location of the trial areas undertaken is shown in Figure 6.20.

Soiling to heavily weathered brickwork and sandstone elements was found to be very intransigent and it was clear that a higher level of residual soiling, reflecting the heavier weatherloading of the facade, would need to be accepted. This problem was most pronounced on exposed sandstone elements such as the finials and copings.

Efflorescence occurred again on the brickwork but to a far lesser extent than on the previous elevation, probably due to the lower inherent salt loading on this more heavily washed elevation.

The 15 foot wide circular medallion to the gable at the eastern end of the Cornwall Street elevation, whose foliated decoration was made up of cream-coloured terracotta, could not be successfully cleaned with any combinations of liquid alkali–acid and acid-only products. Excellent results were achieved following the chance investigation of ProSoCo T-1217 Poultice (24 hour dwell) followed by ProSoCo Restoration Cleaner (5 minute dwell) (see Figure 6.25).

Figure 6.27 Masonry above the main entrance on completion of cleaning and surface repair works. The delight of the Victorian detailing can be appreciated once again.

The last elevation

Cleaning of the final elevation facing Edmund Street did not start before spot trials had confirmed the applicability of the existing specification.

Conclusions

The Faculty of Art and Design demonstrated the complexity of cleaning a facade which is architecturally intricate and includes several material types. The investigations and trials were critical to the preparation of the detailed specification which in turn was an important datum for supervision and costing. Modifications to the specification, made necessary by the many different cleaning conditions that presented themselves as the project progressed, were a sobering reminder of how easily the cleaning could have gone wrong had untested assumptions been applied throughout. The project was also good testimony of the many variations in soiling tenacity that are present on different facades and within the one facade.

The success of the work was due largely to the high level of supervision of the cleaning contractor and her ability to adapt to the many and varied requirements of the cleaning. The specialist technical advice was on call which enabled swift response to any new problems which arose. Of essential value to the work was the good working relationships between the architect, the technical advisor, the cleaning subcontractor and the main contractor.

More detailed pre- and post-testing analysis would have enabled more problems to have been anticipated and eliminated, certainly at earlier stages than they were on the basis of site work alone. The final result has received widespread acclaim, including a Commendation under the Birmingham Design Awards of 1992.

References

1. ProSoCo Inc. Laboratory Report, February 6, 1991. Kansas City: ProSoCo Inc.

6.4 CASE STUDY 4: BUILDING 1, BREL
SWINDON – FACADES COMPRISING
SANDSTONE, LIMESTONE AND BRICK

Figure 6.28 Portion of the facade of Building 1, Swindon, which faces the main rail artery of the West Country, before cleaning and repair. The industrial architecture of the building is highlighted at second-floor level by two carved panels depicting trains. Methods used for the cleaning of these were different from those for the more robust masonry of the remaining walling.

A complex of buildings which once housed the offices and train manufacturing facilities of the Great Western Railway at Swindon, Wiltshire, were given new life in the early 1990s as their conservation, repair and refurbishment began in preparation for new occupants. Located adjacent to Swindon Railway Station, the buildings date from the mid-nineteenth century, their industrial design reflecting the pragmatism of their original uses.

Several individual buildings on the site are listed. These include the former offices complex known as Building 1 which was selected by the Royal Commission for Historic Monuments in England (RCHME) as its new headquarters. Architects for the project were D.Y. Davies Associates of Richmond. The site was owned and developed by Tarmac Swindon Ltd.

Background and brief

The specialist technical advice of Adriel Consultancy was sought regarding preparation of documentation for the cleaning and surface repair package. This required completion of the following brief:

Phase 1

1. To inspect the external masonry of each elevation of Building 1 to determine:
   (a) The characteristics of the masonry of the various eras of construction and the types of stone and other masonry used.
   (b) The overall condition of the stonework and its joints.
   (c) The effect of lack of maintenance and previous remedial works and the need to 'undo' these.
   (d) The nature of soiling and other applied treatments and the observed effect of these on the masonry.
   (e) The range of masonry remedial and repair works appropriate to the Building 1 stonework, the extent and location of these, as far as reasonably possible, on the basis of access and the ability to inspect wall surfaces at close range.
2. To undertake on-site cleaning trials to establish the most appropriate and non-damaging materials and methods for cleaning the range of stone and masonry types present, without adversely affecting any existing pointing in no immediate need of repointing. As complete a range as

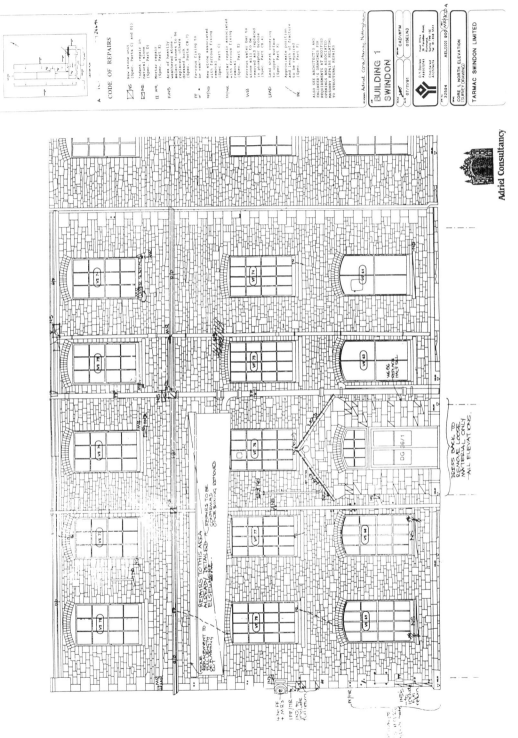

Figure 6.29 Traditional masonry repairs to be undertaken in conjunction with the cleaning were identified on a stone-by-stone basis.

possible of masonry types and soiling conditions were to be
selected, and all trials were to be undertaken at ground level.
3. To undertake on-site pointing inspection works.
4. To prepare a report which recorded the conditions observed,
reasons for the extent and nature of the deterioration under
way, and the recommendations made regarding appropriate
and necessary remedial works.
5. To prepare a preliminary report to accompany listed buildings
submission.

Phase 2

6. To present and discuss the findings of phase 1 on site.
7. To integrate information received from the structural en-
gineers regarding the surface repair of the masonry, as available
during the time of the investigations, trials and document
preparation.
8. To prepare documentation (marked up elevational drawings,
specifications and schedules as appropriate) for the cleaning
and repair works to be undertaken by specialist remedial
contractors. Remedial works were deemed to involve masonry
repair and cleaning, including repointing and the redress of
moisture ingress through the external masonry walling.

Phase 3

9. Following the commencement of work on site, to undertake
site inspections in conjunction with the architects during the
contract period of the external cleaning and repair works.
10. Additional liaison with the structural engineer with regard to
structural matters affecting the external walls.

The inspections and trials described above were undertaken over the
period November 1991 to January 1992.

Nature of the stones

Building 1 comprised abutting buildings three and four storeys in
height. The architecture of each elevation was essentially plain walls
broken up by the frequent and regular placement of windows. The
repetitive facade design was similar in each phase of construction. The
materials and surfaces to the bulk of the facades were robust. The exceptions were the small portion believed to be oldest part of Building 1

Figure 6.30 Detail of conditions present on a section of wall comprising sandstone (upper portion) and limestone (lower portion). Prior to cleaning it was necessary to remove loose pieces of sandstone ashlar and all the pointing as this masked the edges of most stones. Repointing was undertaken as necessary on completion of cleaning.

and two carved panels depicting railway engines transported from original placement elsewhere.

The external masonry was made up of a combination of limestone and sandstone with a limited use of bricks as arched window heads. Limestone was used for gutter cornices, copings, string courses, window sills and jambs, quoins and some limited areas of ashlar. The remainder of the ashlar was of sandstone. The surfaces of the limestone units were dressed. The sandstone ashlar units had split and rock-faced surfaces were laid in an irregularly coursed pattern.

The sandstone ashlar had weathered to a wide range of surface colours ranging from purple, olive green to buff, orange and tan. It was clear that if such a wide range of colours could develop on one type of stone, its mineral constituents were highly mobile and would therefore be sensitive to a chemical cleaning operation. Three samples of sandstone and one of limestone were sent for specialist geological identification to obtain a fuller understanding of the constituents and characteristics that were causing the deterioration and soiling patterns observed. The findings are presented in the Appendix on p. 225, below.

The limestone was confirmed as an oolitic limestone, one of the Bath stones. All three sandstone samples were confirmed as being a Pennant Grit from the Forest of Dean area. This stone was composed predominantly of grains of quartz (about 30 per cent by volume) and fine-grained sedimentary rock fragments with a minor proportion of feldspar. A little ferruginous clay matrix was present and dolomitic carbonate cement was locally abundant. These results confirmed that chemical cleaning of the sandstone would need to be undertaken with great caution.

Condition of the masonry surfaces

Limestone

On the whole, the limestone units were in weathered but good condition. The surfaces of most blocks were granulated. In areas of heaviest weathering, soft beds and pockets had weathered out and harder veins protruded from their more weathered background. Repairs scheduled for the limestone included stone replacement, indent repairs and mortar repairs.

On the weathered elevations of the building, the surfaces of the limestone blocks were very lightly soiled only. At lower levels, where adjacent buildings limited the full impact of the weather and on protected elevations, adherent soiling ranged from moderate to very thick. Joints between the limestone dressings were narrow and in many instances remained in good condition. It was important that the proposed cleaning did not disturb them.

There was a marked difference between the soiling and weathering of the limestone of the dressings and the limestone ashlar of sections of the earliest walling. It was clear at an early stage that the cleaning of the two types of surface needed to be approached differently.

Bricks

The impervious and highly vitrified nature of the blue bricks meant that these were in very good condition and only lightly soiled. In most instances, the black mortar in between was in weathered but acceptable condition.

Sandstone

The sandstone units were in a wide variety of conditions. While the same type of stone had been used throughout, the sizes and shapes of blocks changed as coursing ranged from slightly to very irregularly coursed. Joint widths ranged from ½ in. to 1½ in. Areas with a predominance of small stone units had joints of up to 2½ in. width. In all areas, the original block mortar had been overpointed in a wide strap profile which covered the arrises and wide margins at the edges of every stone. Cutting out trials conducted on each elevation confirmed the strap pointing to be loosely attached and readily removable. This was necessary to enable localized repointing of the mortar behind and, in the first instance, to uncover the substantial widths of soiled stone covered by the repointing prior to cleaning.

Soiling on the sandstone had collected most heavily on the individual stones which protruded most from the wall line and within all the stones in areas which were most frequently wetted. When viewed at long range, variations in the sandstone soiling were much less noticeable. At both close range and long distance, the different stone colours were distinctly visible.

Areas of sandstone affected by run-off from limestone quoins and sills had experienced advanced surface granulation due to the gypsum run-off from above. Surfaces to these stones had weathered back and kept clean by the on-going salt crystallization damage. Elsewhere, the surfaces of stones which were face-bedded were experiencing delamination and detachment of their outer zones. Stones which had been correctly bedded demonstrated smaller-scale losses mainly to their perimeters and the selective loss of softer bands. All loosely adherent material needed to be removed by skilled masons using hand-held tools prior to cleaning.

Figure 6.31 On-site cleaning trial on sandstone ashlar. Loose pointing has been removed from within the area outlined.

On-site cleaning trials

A series of on-site cleaning trials was conducted in January 1992 on representative areas of masonry type and degrees of soiling. A mild, wet abrasive cleaning process was selected.

Water washing had been eliminated because of the relatively low proportion of limestone surfaces present, the potential for water penetration through defective joints and the likelihood of efflorescence appearing on saturated sandstone. Medium and high pressure water processes were eliminated because of the differential hardness between sandstone and limestone surfaces, the vulnerability of joint material generally and the sensitivity of some of the weathered sandstone surfaces. Chemical cleaning was eliminated from consideration because of the incompatibility of cleaning processes required for sandstone and limestone (the acidic cleaner for sandstone strongly etches limestone), the high iron content of the stone and its observed sensitivity to an acidic environment (ability to change colour) and the sandstone's known poor response to chemical cleaning.

The services of a specialist contractor experienced in wet abrasive cleaning were engaged to undertake the trials which were observed throughout by Adriel Consultancy.

The trials investigated the effectiveness of fine and medium-fine manufactured grits at various flow rates and a range of pressures from 10 to 40 psi. Work distances of 12 to 18 in. were used. Both abrasives had angular grains, hardness 5–6 Mohs and density 2.8 kg/dm^{-3}. The fine abrasive was graded from 0.40 mm down, and the medium-fine from 1.0 mm down. The abrasives were J-Blast Finesse and J-Blast SC. Water for the cleaning was provided by a wet shroud head fitted to the nozzle. The wet head was removed at frequent intervals to rinse down the test area and the visor of the operative. There was continuous voice contact between the operative at the nozzle and the operative at the abrasive pot enabling instantaneous adjustment of air pressure and aggregate and water flow rates.

Test areas included sandstone ashlar on three elevations with interspersed dressed limestone quoins and plinth. Areas of heavily soiled limestone ashlar were also included.

The limestone of the dressings was found to be considerably softer than either the sandstone or limestone ashlar adjacent. It was necessary to use the fine abrasive at pressures up to 25 psi and a light to moderate flow rate to clean these surfaces. The work needed to be conducted at a slow pace to accommodate variations in surface weathering and the presence of soft beds and pockets present on each stone surface.

When the method for cleaning the dressed limestone was transferred to the limestone ashlar, cleaning was achieved at an exceedingly slow pace, even when the aggregate flow rate and pressure were increased. The medium-fine aggregate was then investigated and found to produce good results when used at pressures of up to 30 psi. Because of the multi-faceted profile of the stone faces, the cleaning needed to involve at least six passes coming from different directions for all parts to be cleaned.

The abrasive and water streams for the limestone ashlar needed to be kept off the limestone dressings, otherwise damage occurred. This was achieved by cleaning a margin of ashlar beyond the edge of the dressings, avoiding the need to bring the ashlar abrasive and water streams near to the dressings. The medium-fine aggregate was also found to be suitable for the sandstone ashlar. There, it could be used at a higher pressure of 45 psi. The sandstone trial areas included the cutting out of defective pointing and the dressing back of loose stone surface material.

The visual effect of the cleaned limestone dressings was considered attractive, especially as the many subtle variations in surface colour and texture were retained. The impact of the removal of continuous, thick, encrusted soiling from the limestone ashlar was startling. Cleaning of the sandstone revealed its general grey-brown hue and the orange, brown, green and purple colours of the individual stones. The specification for the recommended cleaning procedures set out the details for each type of masonry.

The cleaning of the two carved train panels was considered separately from the remainder of the walling masonry. Close inspection of the surfaces showed much of the crispness of the finer detail to have been lost. The carvings had also had small-scale stone indent repairs undertaken. Thick, encrusted soiling was found within the deep recesses

Figure 6.32 South elevation of Building 1 on completion of masonry cleaning and repair. The sandstone surfaces have been greatly lightened by the cleaning, and streaking has been removed from the limestone.

of the carving. A conservation-oriented approach was recommended for the carved panels, undertaken by a stone conservator rather than the specialist cleaning contractor. It was fortunate that the site was in the part of the UK where the conservative cleaning and surface repair of carved limestone is a well-established practice.

It was recommended that cleaning be undertaken by the use of nebulous water sprays to soften soiling and brushing with small, fine, compact, crinkle-wired phosphor bronze brushes or soft, natural bristle brushes, backed up if necessary by the use of plain clay poultices. The application of limewater to consolidate the friable limestone was recommended to be undertaken before, during and after the cleaning, as appropriate. Select mortar repairs were to be undertaken in a colour-matched, compatible aggregate : lime mortar. It was stressed that all missing detail was not to be reinstated, particularly if there was in-adequate evidence of its original form. Mortar repairs were to be used to make good areas which would otherwise become sources of deterioration. The work was to be finished with the application of a lime : casein shelter coat. All these procedures of cleaning and repair which are widely practised by limestone conservators are known collectively as the Lime Method.

Work on the external masonry was undertaken in 1992–93.

APPENDIX TO CASE STUDY 4

STONE IDENTIFICATION AND ANALYSIS

Report on specimens of stone from the BREL Building, Swindon
Francis G. Dimes, MSc, BSc, MIGeol, FGS
(20th January 1991)

All specimens were examined by eye and with the aid of a ×10 lens and a binocular microscope. Simple physical and chemical tests also were undertaken. Following initial examination and a possible determination as to nature and provenance, all specimens were closely compared with material from known geological horizons and provenance.

One specimen was submitted for a thin section to be prepared and for a photomicrograph to be taken, as well as a petrographic description.

Specimen 1 (limestone) may be described as a buff-coloured (very close to 10YR 8/2 [Munsell System] 'very pale orange' on the Rock Color Chart) highly calcareous stone displaying an oolitic structure, with the ooliths showing a softer, outer somewhat powdery layer and with the 'kernel' of the ooliths mostly missing, thus leaving the broken surfaces of the specimen with a dimpled look. Comminuted fossil matter is irregularly present leading to an irregular grain appearance.

The general appearance, mineral content and overall texture and structure of the specimen are not inconsistent with the sample being an example of *Bath Stone*.

The lithology of specimen 1 suggested it was either Combe Down Stone, Odd Down Stone or Box Ground Stone (Corsham–Box area).

Specimen 2 may be described as a reddish-brown (close to 5R 4/2 'grayish red' on the Rock Color Chart) fairly fine- and even-grained, the grains being subangular and mostly of the mineral quartz with scattered lighter-pink coloured grains, possibly feldspar, prominent. Occasional flakes of white mica (muscovite) may be seen particularly on freshly broken surfaces. The specimen was determined to be a *sandstone* and, from the angularity of the grains, the variety *grit*.

The specimen was noted to be laminated, the laminations being in the plane of the maximum dimension, and also was somewhat friable, suggesting that the stone from which the sample was taken is a fissile sandstone/grit.

The description of the specimen indicates characteristics which are not incompatible with material taken from the geological horizon known as the *Pennant Grit*. In an endeavour to secure the determination, specimen 2 was submitted for a thin section to be made and for a photomicrograph to be taken. The detailed petrographic description supported an identification of Pennant Grit. See petrographic report which follows.

Specimen 3 may be described as a mottled, mostly blue-grey (near to N4 'medium dark gray' on the Rock Color Chart) with areas of brown (near to 5YR 4/4 'moderate brown' laminated (representing original bedding), with bedding planes, top and bottom a rusty colour (between 10YR 5/4 'moderate yellowish brown' and 10YR 4/2 'dark yellowish brown') with white mica (muscovite) flakes lying flat on the bedding planes in marked quantity. The bulk of the stone is of sub-angular grains of quartz with subsidiary feldspar.

Apart from its colour, specimen 3 was determined to be the same as specimen 2, *Pennant Grit*. The determination was considered sufficiently secure for a thin section not to be cut.

Specimen 4 was found on examination to be of the same nature as specimens 2 and 3, and hence a determination of *Pennant Grit* is given.

The Pennant Grit is a formation within the Coal Measures Series, Carboniferous in age. In South Wales, in the Forest of Dean, in Monmouth and in the Bristol coalfield area of Avon and Somerset, the Coal Measures Series is divided into an upper and lower series separated by a thick group of sandstones – the Pennant Series or the Pennant Grit – which in the main are massive 'blue-grey' or 'red', rusty weathering and parted at intervals by thick shale beds. Some of the beds may be very coarsely grained. In places, the rock may be fissile and closely laminated enough for it to be considered for use as a tilestone.

Because the stone generally is tough and durable, particularly when massive, it has been widely used for building, for example in Bristol (the jail), Cardiff (in Park House, Park Place), Caerphilly Castle, South Wales generally, Portishead and elsewhere.

From comparison with material of known provenance, gross appearance and mineral content, the submitted specimens visually match most closely samples from the Forest of Dean area, specimen 2 matching particularly well with 'Red Forest of Dean Stone'.

The petrography of a sample of delaminating sandstone from a building in Swindon
Robin W. Sanderson, BSc

Analytical methods

Analysis has been effected by means of microscopical examination of a 30μm thick section treated with sodium cobaltinitrite stain to differentiate between feldspar mineral phases, low magnification examination of the hand-specimen and by simple chemical tests. The sectioned sample was impregnated with coloured resin to show empty pore-space in the thin section. In the following description, colour terminology follows that of the Geological Society of America Rock Color Chart, 1970.

Identification of the stone

The sample is a medium-grained, feldspathic litharenite.

Mineral composition

The stone is composed predominantly of grains of quartz (c. 30 vol.%) and fine-grained sedimentary rock fragments, with a minor proportion of feldspar. A little detrital clay matrix is present and dolomitic carbonate cement is locally abundant.

Petrographical description: macroscopical features:

The fragmentary weathered sample is of slightly friable and roughly laminated nature, with a uniform colour between 'pale red' (5R 6/2) and 'grayish red' (5R 4/2), apart from rare, small, pale greenish, bleached spots less than 2 mm across. Viewed at low magnification, distinct pink and green grains are noticeable. An ovoid depression, c. 13 mm across, lined with ferruginous clay, apparently represents a mould of a pebble. No reaction to the test for calcite was noted.

Petrographical description: microscopical features

The stone has a poorly sorted grain supported and moderately to strongly compacted detrital fabric. Very angular to subangular grains of low sphericity measure up to 640 μm, modal medium sand (lower) grade (250-350 μm). There is a slight indication of subparallel arrangement of elongate grains.

Monocrystalline quartz is only weakly strained, but strained polycrystalline quartz is common, as is chert. Some vein quartz is present. Lithic fragments include mainly fine-grained impure sandstones and mudstones, some of which are phyllitic and more or less chloritic. Haematite, or ferruginous mudstone is common. Rarer fine metamorphic types – quartz–garnet and quartz chlorite rocks – are also present. Feldspars are moderately abundant with K-feldspar apparently dominant. Accessory minerals are rare but include muscovite and chlorite flakes and garnet grains.

Detrital grains show incomplete pellicles of ferruginous clay (mixed chlorite/illite) matrix. A pore-filling, partly replacive, medium crystalline dolomitic cement is locally abundant.

The sample exhibits weathering-induced secondary fracture-porosity, but little if any visible primary macroporosity.

Comments

Assuming that the sample is a British stone, the macroscopical features suggest either one of Old Red Sandstone or a ferruginized Pennant Sandstone. The relatively low quartz content and high proportion of fine sedimentary rock grains are characteristic of the Pennant type of stone. These are usually of a grey or greenish tint, the red colouration being associated with the areas of haematite mineralization of the Forest of Dean and Bristol areas. The presence of pebbles is very unusual in Pennant sandstones.

Bibliography

Amoroso, G.G. and Fassina, V. (1983) *Stone Decay and Conservation: Atmospheric Pollution, Cleaning, Consolidation and Protection*, Materials and Science Monograph II. Amsterdam: Elsevier, pp. 254–270.

Andrew, C. (1992) Towards an Aesthetic Theory of Building Soiling, *Stone Cleaning and the Nature, Soiling and Decay Mechanisms of Stone*, Proceedings of the International Conference held in Edinburgh, UK, 14–16 April 1992. London: Donhead, pp. 63–81.

Andrew, C. and Crawford, E. (1992) Conservation and Planning Considerations in Stone Cleaning, *Stone Cleaning and the Nature, Soiling and Decay Mechanisms of Stone*, Proceedings of the International Conference held in Edinburgh, UK, 14–16 April 1992. London: Donhead, pp. 193–198.

Ashurst, J. (1985) Cleaning and Surface Repair – Past Mistakes and Future Prospects, *APT*, Vol. XVII, No. 2, pp. 39–41.

Ashurst, J. (1990) Cleaning Masonry Buildings, *Conservation of Building and Decorative Stone*, Vol. 2. London: Butterworth/Heinemann, pp. 125–34.

Ashurst, J. and N. (1988) *Practical Building Conservation – English Heritage Technical Handbook*, Aldershot: Gower Technical Press. Volume 1: *Stone Masonry*; Volume 2: *Brick, Terracotta and Earth*; Volume 3: *Mortars, Plasters and Renders*; Volume 4: *Metals*; Volume 5: *Wood, Glass and Resins*.

Ashurst, J. and Dimes, F.G. (eds) (1990) *Conservation of Building and Decorative Stone*, Vols 1 and 2. London: Butterworth/Heinemann.

Ashurst, N. (1990) Paint Removals: Problems and Solutions, *The Architects' Journal*, Vol. 191, No. 18, pp. 67–75.

Ashurst, N. and J. (1991) *Cleaning Stone and Brick*; Technical Pamphlet 4. London: SPAB.

Ashurst, N. and Kelly, J. (1990) The Analytical Approach to Stone, Its Cleaning, Repair and Treatment, *Conservation of Building and Decorative Stone*, Vol. 2. London: Butterworth/Heinemann, pp. 240–43.

Ball, D.J. (1987) Particulate Carbon Emissions and Diesel Vehicles, Report C337/87, London Scientific Services, *Conference Proceedings: The Soiling of Buildings and Deterioration in Urban Areas*. Enfield: Middlesex Polytechnic, Faculty of Engineering, Science and Mathematics, Centre for Urban Pollution Research.

Ball, D.J. (1987) Black Lungs and Black Walls, *New Scientist*, 12 February, pp.28–29.

Ball, D.J. and Hume, R. (1977) The Relative Importance of Vehicular and Domestic Emissions of Dark Smoke in Greater London in the Mid-1970s, *Atmospheric Environment*, Vol.11, pp.1065–1073.

Berryman, N.D. and Tindall, Susan M. (1984) *Terra Cotta: Preservation of an Historic Building Material*. Landmarks Preservation Council of Illinois, USA.

Bidwell, T. (1977) *The Conservation of Brick Buildings*. London: Brick Development Association.

Bluck, B. (1992) The Composition and Weathering of Sandstone in Relation to Cleaning, *Stone Cleaning and the Nature, Soiling and Decay Mechanisms of Stone*, Proceedings of the International Conference held in Edinburgh, UK, 14–16 April 1992. London: Donhead, pp.125–127.

Bluck, B.J. and Porter, J. (1991) Sandstone Buildings and Cleaning Problems, *Stone Industries*, March, pp.21–27.

Bluck, B.J. and Porter, J. (1991) Aims and Methods of Sandstone Cleaning, *Stone Industries*, April, pp.21–28.

Boyer, D.W. (1986) Masonry Cleaning: The State of the Art, *Cleaning Stone and Masonry. ASTM STP 935*. Philadelphia: American Society for Testing and Materials.

Bravery, A.F., Berry, R.W., Carey, J.K. and Cooper, D.E. (1987) *Recognising Wood Rot and Insect Damage in Buildings: Building Establishment Report*. Princes Risborough: Building Research Establishment.

Brick Development Association (1982) Building Note 2, *Cleaning of Brickwork*. Windsor: BDA.

Brimblecombe, P. (1992) A Brief History of Grime: Accumulation and Removal of Soot Deposits on Buildings Since the 17th Century, *Stone Cleaning and the Nature, Soiling and Decay Mechanisms of Stone*, Proceedings of the International Conference held in Edinburgh, UK, 14–16 April 1992. London: Donhead, pp.53–62.

British Standards Institution (1969) BS 3826 *Silicone-Based Water Repellents for Masonry*. London: BSI.

British Standards Institution (1982) BS 6270 *Cleaning and Surface Repair of Buildings. Part 1, Natural Stone, Cast Stone and Clay and Calcium Silicate Brick Masonry*. London: BSI.

British Standards Institution (1984) BS 6477 *Water Repellents for Masonry Surfaces*. London: BSI.

British Standards Institution (1986) BS 3761 *Non-flammable Solvent-based Paint Remover*. London: BSI.

The Builders Employers Confederation (1989) *COSHH in Construction: The BEC General Assessment File*. London: BEC

Building Research Station (1971) *Colourless Treatments for Masonry: Digest 125*. Garston: HMSO.

Building Research Station (1982) *Control of Lichens, Moulds and Similar Growths*, Digest 139. Garston: HMSO.

Building Research Station (1983) *Cleaning External Surfaces of Buildings*, Digest 280. Garston: HMSO.

Building Research Station (1989) *The Selection of Natural Building Stone*, Digest 269. Garston: HMSO.

Building Research Station (1990) *Decay and Conservation of Stone Masonry*, Digest 177. Garston: HMSO.

Butcher, R. (1993) A Case for Traditional and Natural Paints and Coatings, *SPAB News*, Vol.14, No.2, pp.14–17.

Butlin, R.N. (1985) Further Perspectives on Acid Rain: Effects of Acid Deposition on UK Buildings, *NSCA 52nd Annual Conference, Scarborough*. Garston: Building Research Establishment.

Butlin, R., Russell, C. and McCaig, I. (1992) The Removal of Graffiti, *Stone Cleaning and the Nature, Soiling and Decay Mechanisms of Stone*, Proceedings of the International Conference held in Edinburgh, UK, 14–16 April 1992. London: Donhead (full text issued at Conference), pp.307–308.

Chang, Shine (1990) Methylene Chloride Poisoning in Furniture Strippers, *Art Hazard News*, Vol.13, No.3, p.4, as quoted in *Art and Archaeology Technical Abstracts*, Vol.28, No. 1, 1991, p.42.

Charles, Prince of Wales (1989) *Vision of Britain: A Personal View of Architecture*. London: Doubleday.

Chemical Industries Association (1991) *Chemical Exposure Treatment Cards*. London: CIA Publications.

Chevin, D. (1992) All Features Great and Small, *Building*, 27 November, pp.36–40.

Clarke, B.L. (1972) Some Recent Research in Cleaning External Masonry in Great Britain, *The Treatment of Stone*. Bologna: Centro per la conservazione delle sculture all'aperto.

Clifton, J.R. (ed.) (1983) *Cleaning Stone and Masonry*, symposium sponsored by ASTM Committee E-6 on Performance of Building Constructions, Louisville, Kentucky, 18 April 1983. Philadelphia: ASTM Publications.

Clifton, J.R. and Godette, M. (1983) Performance Tests for Graffiti Removers, *Cleaning Stone and Masonry*, symposium sponsored by ASTM Committee E-6 on Performance of Building Constructions, Louisville, Kentucky, 18 April 1983, pp.14–24. Philadelphia: ASTM Publications.

Construction Industries Research and Information Association (CIRIA) (1981) *A Guide to the Safe Use of Chemicals in Construction*. London: CIRIA.

Construction Industry Advisory Committee (CONIAC) (1988) *Managing Health and Safety in Construction: Management Contracting*. London: HMSO.

Construction Industry Advisory Committee (CONIAC) (1990) *The Control of Substances Hazardous to Health in the Construction Industry*. London: HMSO.

Cox, A. (1988) Bricks to Build a Capital, in *Good and Proper Materials: The Fabric of London Since the Great Fire.* Paper given at a conference organized by the Survey of London at the Society of Antiquaries, 21 October 1988, edited by Hermione Hobhouse and Ann Saunder. Royal Commission on the Historical Monuments of England in Association with the London Topographical Society, Publication No. 140, 1989, pp.3–15.

Crawford, E. (1992) Coming Clean, *Context No.35 (Journal of the Association of Conservation Officers)*, September, pp.19–20.

Fidler, J. (1988) Stain Reaction, *Traditional Homes*, November, pp.127–131.

Fry, M.F (1983) Exterior Cleaning by Microblasting, *Stone Industries*, Jan./Feb. 1983, pp.20–21.

Gauri, K.L., Holdren, G.C. and Vaughan, W.C. (1983) Cleaning Efflorescences from Masonry, *Cleaning Stone and Masonry*, symposium sponsored by ASTM Committee E-6 on Performance of Building Constructions, Louisville, Kentucky, 18 April 1983. Philadelphia: ASTM Publications, pp.3–13.

Gauri, K.L., Parks, L., Jaynes, J. and Atlas, R. (1992) Removal of Sulphated-crust from Marble using Sulphate-reducing Bacteria, *Stone Cleaning and the Nature, Soiling and Decay Mechanisms of Stone*, Proceedings of the International Conference held in Edinburgh, UK, 14–16 April 1992. London: Donhead, pp.160–165.

Grant, C. and Bravery, A.F. (1981) Laboratory Evaluation of Algicidal Biocides for Use on

Constructional Materials. 1: An Assessment of Some Current Test Methods, *International Biodeterioration Bulletin*, Vol.17, No. 4, pp.113–123.

Grimmer, A.E. (1979) *Dangers of Abrasive Cleaning to Historic Buildings: Preservation Briefs 6*, Technical Preservation Services Division, Heritage Conservation and Recreation Service. Washington: US Government Printing Office.

Harding, J.R. and Smith, R.A. (1986) *Cleaning of Brickwork: BDA Building Note 2*. Windsor: Brick Development Association.

Hart, D. (1988) *The Building Magnesian Limestones of the British Isles*, Building Research Establishment Report. London: HMSO.

Health and Safety Executive (1990) *Introducing COSHH: A Brief Guide for all Employers to the New Requirements for Controlling Hazardous Substances in the Workplace Introduced in the Control of Substances Hazardous to Health Regulations 1988 (COSHH)*. London: HMSO.

Health and Safety Executive (1990) *Introducing Assessment: A Simplified Guide for Employers, Control of Substances Hazardous to Health Regulations 1988 (COSHH)*. London: HMSO.

Health and Safety Executive (1990) *Hazard and Risk Explained. Control of Substances Hazardous to Health Regulations 1988 (COSHH)*. London: HMSO.

Health and Safety Executive (1990) *Solvents and You*. London: HMSO.

Health and Safety Executive (1993) *A Step-by-step Guide to COSHH*. London: HMSO.

Health and Safety Executive (1993) *COSHH: A Brief Guide for Employers*. London: HMSO.

Health and Safety Executive (1993) *Toxicology of Substances in Relation to Major Hazards: Hydrogen Fluoride*, (revised). London: HMSO.

Heller, H.L. (1977) The Chemistry of Masonry Cleaning, *APT*, Vol.IX, No.2, pp.2–9.

Hempel, K. (1978) The Biological Pack, *Alteration et Protection des Monuments en Pierre*. Paris: UNESCO/RILEM.

Heuman, J. (1992) Removing Corrosion on a Painted Outdoor Bronze Sculpture with Mild Chelating Agents, *The Conservator*, No. 16.

Hirst, E. (1991) Marble and Alabaster Cleaning and Polishing, pp.37–40, contribution to 'Surrey House, Norwich: The Repair of An Edwardian Building', *ASCHB Transactions*, Vol.16, pp.25–40.

Honeyborne, D.B. and Price, C.A. (1980) Decay Mechanisms in Porous Limestones, Parts 1 and 2, *SPAB News*, No. 1, pp.1–5, 23, 31.

Honeyborne, D., Ashurst, J., Price, C. and Ross, K. (1990) Surface Treatments, in Ashurst, J. and Dimes, F.C. (eds), *Conservation of Building and Decorative Stone*, Vol.2. London: Butterworth/Heinemann, pp.155–84.

Honeyborne, D.B. (1990) Weathering and Decay of Masonry, in Ashurst, J. and Dimes, F.C. (eds), *Conservation of Building and Decorative Stone*, Vol.1. London: Butterworth-Heinemann, pp.153–78.

Hunt, B. and Miglio, B. (1992) Deterioration of Stone Floors, *Stone Industries*, July/August, pp.21–26.

Hutton, T.C. and Dobson, J. (1992) The Control of Feral Pigeons: An Independent Approach, *Structural Survey*, Vol.II, No.2, Autumn, pp.159–167.

Kelly, J. (1989) The Petrographic Microscope as an Aid to Stone Conservation, *Microscopy and Analysis*, June.

Kelsall, F. (1988) Stucco, in *Good and Proper Materials: The Fabric of London Since the Great Fire*. Paper given at a conference organized by the Survey of London at the Society of Antiquaries on 21 October 1988, edited by Hermione Hobhouse and Ann Saunder. Royal Commission on the Historical Monuments of England in Association with the London Topographical Society, Publication No. 140, 1989, pp.18–24.

Larson, J. (1990) The Conservation of Stone Sculpture in Museums, in Ashurst, J. and Dimes, F.G. (eds), *Conservation of Building and Decorative Stone*, Vol.2. London: Butterworth/Heinemann, pp.197–207.

Leary, E. (1983) *The Building Limestones of the British Isles*, Building Research Establishment Report. London: HMSO.

Leary, E. (1986) *The Building Sandstones of the British Isles*, Building Research Establishment Report. London: HMSO.

Liddle, C. (1992) Building Cleaning: Process or Procedure, an Industry View, *Stone Cleaning and the Nature, Soiling and Decay Mechanisms of Stone*, Proceedings of the International Conference held in Edinburgh, UK, 14–16 April 1992. London: Donhead, pp.207–213.

Life After the Regulations (1992) *Stone Industries*, 7 September, pp.28–29.

Livingston, R. (1992) Geochemical Considerations in the Cleaning of Carbonate Stone, *Stone Cleaning and the Nature, Soiling and Decay Mechanisms of Stone*, Proceedings of the International Conference held in Edinburgh, UK, 14–16 April 1992. London: Donhead, pp.166–179,

Lloyd, N. (1983) *A History of English Brickwork*. Woodbridge: Antique Collectors' Club.

McCann, M. (1979) *Artist Beware*. New York: Watson-Guptill.

MacDonald, J., Thomson, B. and Tonge, K. (1992) Chemical Cleaning of Sandstone: Comparative Laboratory Studies, *Stone Cleaning and the Nature, Soiling and Decay Mechanisms of Stone*, Proceedings of the International Conference held in Edinburgh, UK, 14–16 April 1992. London: Donhead, pp.217–226.

McLaughlin, D. (1989) Paint Removal from Bath Stone, *ASCHB Transactions*, Vol.14, pp.49–52.

McLaughlin, D. (1992) 'Acid Rain': the Cleaning and Conservation of Stonework in Bath, *Stone Cleaning and the Nature, Soiling and Decay Mechanisms of Stone*, Proceedings of the International Conference held in Edinburgh, UK, 14–16 April 1992. London: Donhead. pp.183–192.

Mack, R.C. (1975) *The Cleaning and Waterproof Coating of Masonry Buildings: Preservation Briefs 1*, Technical Preservation Services Division, Heritage Conservation and Recreation Service. Washington: US Government Printing Office.

Mack, R.C. (1983) Cleaning and Waterproofing of Historic Masonry Buildings, *Cleaning Stone and Masonry*, a symposium sponsored by ASTM Committee E-6 on Performance of Building Constructions, Louisville, Kentucky, 18 April 1983, pp.96–106, Philadelphia: ASTM Publications.

Mansfield, T.A. (1986) Soiling of London's Buildings, *London Environmental Bulletin*, Spring, pp.6–7.

Mansfield, T.A. (1988) Building Soiling and the Stone Cleaning Industry, *Stone Industries*, April, pp.24–26.

Mansfield, T.A. (1992) Sources of Building Soiling and a Review of the Stone Cleaning Industry 1991, *Stone Cleaning and the Nature, Soiling and Decay Mechanisms of Stone*, Proceedings of the International Conference held in Edinburgh, UK, 14–16 April 1992. London: Donhead, pp.84–93.

Martin, D.T. (1992) *Stone Cleaning in Glasgow*, statement issued 15th April to International Conference on Stone Cleaning, Heriot-Watt University, Edinburgh.

Maxwell, I. (1992) Stone Cleaning, for Better or Worse? An Overview, *Stone Cleaning and the Nature, Soiling and Decay Mechanisms of Stone*, Proceedings of the International Conference held in Edinburgh, UK, 14–16 April 1992. London: Donhead. pp.3–49.

Microbe Cocktails Star in Disaster Troubleshooter's Arsenal (1991) *Building*, 1 March, p.47.

Middlesex Polytechnic (1987) *Conference Proceedings: The Soiling of Buildings and Deterioration in Urban Areas*. Enfield: Middlesex Polytechnic, Faculty of Engineering, Science and Mathematics, Centre for Urban Pollution Research.

Moncrieff, A. and Weaver, G. (1983) *Science for Conservators Book 2, Cleaning*, Crafts Council

Conservation Science Teaching Series. London: Crafts Council.

Mora, P. and Mora, L. (1971) Metodo per la Rimozione di Incrostazioni su Pietre Calcaree e su Dipinti Murali, *Problemi di Conservazione*. Bologna: Editrice Compositori, pp. 3–49.

Moss, P. (1990) The Use of Air-abrasive Cleaning Techniques for Stone Building Surfaces, in Ashurst, J. and Dimes, F.G. (eds), *Conservation of Building and Decorative Stone*, Vol. 2. London: Butterworth/Heinemann, pp. 237–239.

Newby, P.T., Mansfield, T.A. and Hamilton, R.S. (1991) Sources and Economic Implications of Building Soiling in Urban Areas, *The Science of the Total Environment*, Vol. 100. Amsterdam: Elsevier. pp. 347–365.

Newey, C., Boff, R., Daniels, V., Pascoe, M. and Tennent, N. (1983) *Science for Conservators. Book 3 Adhesives and Coatings*, Crafts Council Conservation Science Teaching Series. London: Crafts Council.

Orcsik, E. (1984) *Some Theoretical and Practical Problems of the Cleaning of Limestone and Marble*, ICOMOS, Copenhagen, 7th Triennial Meeting. Copenhagen: ICOM Committee for Conservation.

Palmer, R. (1992) Microbiological Damage to Building Stone: Analysis and Intervention, *Stone Cleaning and the Nature, Soiling and Decay Mechanisms of Stone*, Proceedings of the International Conference held in Edinburgh, UK, 14–16 April 1992. London: Donhead, pp. 239–245.

Price, C.A. (1975) Stone Decay and Preservation, *Chemistry in Britain*, Vol. II, pp. 350–353.

Price, C. and Ross, K. (1990) Technical Appraisal of Stone Conservation Techniques at Wells Cathedral, in Ashurst, J. and Dimes, F.G. (eds), *Conservation of Building and Decorative Stone*. London: Butterworth/Heinemann.

Restoring the Beauty Within, *ProSoCo News*, Spring 1989, p. 4.

Robert Gordon Institute of Technology (Masonry Conservation Research Group) (April 1992) *Stone Cleaning in Scotland: Research Commission Investigating the Effects of Cleaning Sandstone*, Research Reports 1–3, Research Summary, Literature Review. Historic Scotland, Scottish Enterprise, and the Robert Gordon Institute of Technology.

Rodwell, D. (1992) Stone Cleaning in Urban Conservation, *Stone Cleaning and the Nature, Soiling and Decay Mechanisms of Stone*, Proceedings of the International Conference held in Edinburgh, UK, 14–16 April 1992. London: Donhead, pp. 199–206.

Rossi-Manaresi, R. and Torraca, G. (eds) (1972) *The Treatment of Stone*. Bologna: Centro per la Conservazione delle Sculture all'Aperto.

Rossi-Manaresi, R. and Tucci, A. (1991) Pore Structure and the Disruptive or Cementing Effect of Salt Crystallization in Various Types of Stone, *Studies in Conservation*, Vol. 36, pp. 53–58.

Schaffer, R.J. (1932) *The Weathering of Natural Building Stones*, Building Research Special Report No. 18, Department of Scientific and Industrial Research. London: HMSO.

Skoulikidis, T. and Papakonstantinou, P. (1992) Stone Cleaning by the Inversion of Gypsum back into Calcium Carbonate, *Stone Cleaning and the Nature, Soiling and Decay Mechanisms of Stone*, Proceedings of the International Conference held in Edinburgh, UK, 14–16 April 1992. London: Donhead, pp. 155–159.

Spry, A.H. (1982) *Principles of Cleaning Masonry Buildings*. Melbourne: Australian Council of National Trusts, and National Trust of Australia (Victoria).

Spry, A.H. (1984) Exterior Paint Removal from Buildings, *Heritage Australia*, Summer, pp. 74–77.

Spry, A.H. and West, D.G. (1985) *The Defence Against Graffiti*, AMDEL Report No. 1571. Frewville, SA 5063: AMDEL.

Spry, A.H. and West, D.G. (1986) *The Defence Against Graffiti: Addendum October 1986*. Frewville, SA 5063: AMDEL.

Staehli, A.M. (1986) Appropriate Water Pressures for Masonry Cleaning. What do the numbers mean?, *APT Bulletin*, Vol. XVIII, No. 4, pp. 10–17.

Stambolov, T. and Van Asperen de Boer, J.R.J. (1972) *The Deterioration and Conservation of Porous Building Materials in Monuments*. Rome: International Centre for Conservation.

Stratton, M. (1990) Shining Through the Smog: Terracotta and Faience, in *Good and Proper Materials: The Fabric of London Since the Great Fire*. Paper given at a conference organized by the Survey of London at the Society of Antiquaries on 21 October 1988, edited by Hermione Hobhouse and Ann Saunder. Royal Commission on the Historical Monuments of England in Association with the London Topographical Society, Publication No. 140, 1989.

Straw, T.A. (1990) *Putting the Record Straight*, lecture given at UK Stone Federation Seminar, Edinburgh.

Tiller, D.P. (1979) *The Preservation of Historic Glazed Architectural Terra-cotta*, Preservation Briefs 7, Technical Preservation Services Division, Heritage Conservation and Recreation Service. Washington: US Government Printing Office.

Torraca, G. (1981) *Porous Building Materials: Materials Science for Architectural Conservation*. Rome: ICCROM.

Tucker, C. (1992) The Cleaning of the Palace of Westminster, *Stone Cleaning and the Nature, Soiling and Decay Mechanisms of Stone*, Proceedings of the International Conference held in Edinburgh, UK, 14–16 April 1992. London: Donhead, pp.113–120.

Verhoef, L.G.W. (ed.) (1988) *Soiling and Cleaning of Building Facades: Report of Technical Committee 62 SCF RILEM*. London, New York: Chapman and Hall.

Waite, J.G. and Cheng, R.J. (1983) A Case Study of the Cleaning and Conservation of Marble at the Schenectady, New York, City Hall, *Cleaning Stone and Masonry*, symposium sponsored by ASTM Committee E-6 on Performance of Building Constructions, Louisville, Kentucky, 18 April 1983. Philadelphia: ASTM Publications, pp.107–152.

Weaver, G., Ashley-Smith, J., Roy, A., Staniforth, S. and Barker, H. (1982) *Science for Conservators. Book 1, An Introduction to Materials*, Crafts Council Conservation Science Teaching Series. London: Crafts Council.

Weaver, M.E. (1993) *Cleaning and Conserving Decorative Interior Marblework*, paper presented at the Interiors Conference for Historic Buildings II, Washington DC, 17–19 February, pp.1–32.

Weaver, M.E. and Matero, F.G. (1993) *Conserving Buildings: A Guide to Techniques and Materials*. New York: John Wiley.

Webster, R.G.M. (ed.) (1992) *Stone Cleaning and the Nature, Soiling and Decay Mechanisms of Stone*, Proceedings of the International Conference held in Edinburgh, UK, 14–16 April 1992, London: Donhead.

Weeks, K.D. and Look, D.W. (1982) *Exterior Paint Problems on Historic Woodwork*, Preservation Briefs 10, Technical Preservation Services Division, Heritage Conservation and Recreation Service. Washington: US Government Printing Office.

Weiss, N.R. (1985) *Exterior Cleaning of Historic Masonry Buildings (Draft)*. Washington: National Park Service, United States Department of the Interior.

Whalley, B., Smith, B. and Magee, R. (1992) Effects of Particulate Air Pollutants on Materials: Investigation of Surface Crust Formation, *Stone Cleaning and the Nature, Soiling and Decay Mechanisms of Stone*, Proceedings of the International Conference held in Edinburgh, UK, 14–16 April 1992. London: Donhead, pp.227–234.

Wilimzig, M., Sand, W. and Bock, E. (1992) The Impact of Stone Cleaning on Micro-organisms and Microbially Influenced Corrosion, *Stone Cleaning and the Nature, Soiling and Decay Mechanisms of Stone*, Proceedings of the International Conference held in Edinburgh, UK, 14–16 April 1992. London: Donhead, pp.235–236.

Winkler, E.M. (1973) *Stone: Properties, Durability in Man's Environment*. New York: Springer-Verlag.

Winkler, E.M. (1983) A Macrostereogrammetric Technique for Measuring Surface Erosion

Losses on Stone, *Cleaning Stone and Masonry*, symposium sponsored by ASTM Committee E-6 on Performance of Building Constructions, Louisville, Kentucky, 18 April 1983. Philadelphia: ASTM Publications, pp.153–164.

Wood, P.A. and MacRae, Z.C. (1972) Microbial Activity in Sandstone Deterioration, *Biodeterioration Bulletin*, Vol.8, No.1, pp.25–27.

Yates, T.J.S., Coote, A.T. and Butlin, R.N. (1988) The Effect of Acid Deposition on Buildings and Building Materials, *Construction and Building Materials*, Vol.2, No.1, pp.20–26.

Young, M. and Urquhart, D. (1992) Abrasive Cleaning of Sandstone Buildings and Monuments: An Experimental Investigation, *Stone Cleaning and the Nature, Soiling and Decay Mechanisms of Stone*, Proceedings of the International Conference held in Edinburgh, UK, 14–16 April 1992. London: Donhead, pp.128–140.

Index

The first number given indicates which volume is referred to; page numbers in bold refer to illustrations